Vibrations

For
Health And Happiness

Everyone's Easy Guide To Stress-free Living

by

Tom Bolton

Published by Crown House Publishing

First published in the UK by

Crown House Publishing
Crown Buildings
Bancyfelin
Carmarthen
Wales

© Tom Bolton 1998

The right of Tom Bolton to be identified as the author of this work
has been asserted by him in accordance with the Copyright,
Designs and Patents Act 1988.

First published 1998.

British Library of Cataloguing-in-Publication Data
A catalogue entry for this book is available
from the British Library.

ISBN 1899836160

Printed and bound in Wales by
WBC Book Manufacturers,
Waterton Industrial Estate,
Bridgend, Mid Glamorgan.

I dedicate this book to you Bev (Beverley), my caring, loving, patient friend and partner. Thank you for all the support and help you have given me throughout the writing of this book. Without you it could never have been written.

Acknowledgments

I wish to express my sincere appreciation for all the help and support that I have had in writing this book. In particular, to Glenys and David from Crown House Publishing for their faith in my ability to complete this work on time; to Nicky who proofread and edited the text, and gave me valuable feedback and advice; and to Alex for her calm, confident, and clear communication skills. I would also like to thank the rest of the team behind the scenes at The Anglo-American Book Company.

I would also like to thank Rosemary Larbalestier for writing the foreword and for the excellent lectures that she gave and that I had the good fortune to attend in the late '80s.

Finally I am eternally grateful for everyone else that has shared joys and sorrows with me throughout my stormy life; you are all my teachers. May peace, happiness and good fortune light up your lives, and may your gods go with you on your eternal journey.

Disclaimer

The contents of this book come from Tom Bolton's personal research, discovery, understanding, and years of studying the Ageless Wisdom.

Nothing in this book is meant to reflect in any way the views, ideas, beliefs, creeds or standards of any organisation mentioned in this book, or any body or organisation to which Tom Bolton belongs or has any relationship with in any way.

Keynotes at the beginning of each chapter (except Chapter Three) are verses taken from the author's own poems. Exercises and Chakra positions modelled by Bev (Buffy) Anderson.

Table Of Contents

Human Constitution

- The Meaning Of Life
- Four Essential Life Goals
- The Three Dosha-Forces
- The Qualities Of The Doshas
- The Six Tastes
- Diet
- Digestion
- People Types
- Dosha Type Questionnaire
- Vata, Pitta, Kapha Types
- Three Dosha Types
- Three Reversed Sub-Dosha Types
- Eating For Balance
- Purification Routine
- General Information
- Summary

Building Blocks Of The Body

- Carbohydrates
- Proteins
- Fats
- Fibre
- Tips On Eating
- Vitamins And Minerals
- Oxidisation And Antioxidants
- Enzymes
- Main Vitamins
- Vitamin Supplementation
- Vital Minerals
- Summary

Aromatherapy

- Vital Creative Life Force
- Plants' Vital Forces
- Medical Use Of Plant Extracts
- Aromatherapy In Present Times
- Synergies
- Application
- Inhalation
- Foot Baths
- Baths
- Compresses And Massage
- Essential Oils
- Oil Combinations
- Summary

The Human Energy Centres

- The Chakras
- Muladhara - Route/Base
- Svadhisthana - Sacral
- Manipura - Solar Plexus
- Anahata - Heart/Thymus
- Visuddha - Thyroid/Hollow Of Throat
- Ajna - Brow/Third Eye
- Sahasrara - Padma/Crown
- Kundilini - Vital Force
- Ida, Pingala
- Sushumna
- Energy Balancing Exercises
- Sound Balancing
- Summary

Karma, Reincarnation And Past Lives

- Karma
- The Personality
- Death
- A Scenario Of Between Life States
- Reincarnation
- Karma's Effect On Reincarnation
- Regressions
- Aphorisms From The Ageless Wisdom
- Summary

Conclusion

- My Beliefs
- Poem: *Tips Along Life's Way*
- Finale

Foreword

Some years have rolled by since I first met Tom when, with a small group, we studied together some of the all-embracing facets of The Ageless Wisdom. What marked Tom was his eagerness for knowledge and greater understanding - it seemed to be a hunger within him - and an almost restless desire to be of service and to help people. How good it is to find that the flame of his enthusiasm still burns brightly.

Having experienced, as he puts it, his "Personal Hell", Tom has a natural and ready sympathy with the diversity of human ills that so often form a part of our everyday lives.

The advice and techniques offered in this book cover a fairly broad spectrum, but the author has an easy style and there is an abundance of warm common sense and helpful ideas. The summaries at the close of each chapter serve to focus one on the salient points of the subject matter, and the *Glossary of Terms* is an interesting and helpful addition. I particularly like the way each chapter is prefaced by a brief but potent Keynote called from Wisdom's store of Truth, Goodness and Beauty. O! Reader - pause awhile over them, for their value is great. Likewise the Aphorisms at the close of Chapter Thirteen contain many little gems for those of thoughtful disposition.

I would like to thank Tom for this opportunity to contribute in a small way to his worthwhile endeavour to spread abroad his "Vibrations for Health and Happiness", and I am happy to wish his book well.

Rosemary A. Larbalestier
Wallasey, Wirral.
24th November, 1997

Introduction

Our cosmos is a universe of vital vibrating energy, and each one of us is a small reflection of that universe. When energy is able to move easily all is fine, but should anything restrict this flow, stress may occur. Stress is OK, without it there wouldn't be any life; however, when it reaches overload, trouble is often the result. In my work as a holistic practitioner I see people of all ages who are experiencing discomfort and pain, both mental and physical. Whatever the cause, common factors in most cases are stress overload and tension within the nervous system.

Most of us who live in this high tech society have at some time experienced one or more conditions linked to build-up of stress or tension e.g. aches and pains, bad temper, anxiety, insomnia, depression etc.. This is partly due to the fast pace of life, which can be very challenging and demanding. Modern living is responsible for creating intense pressure on us as beings.

Stress can be likened to water dripping from a tap into a glass. As long as the glass is filling there is no overflow, but when the water reaches the brim, overflow occurs. In order to stop stress overflow, we need to either turn off the tap (not always possible), or tilt the glass at reasonable intervals to lower the level. The good news is that this is far easier to do than you might think.

This book offers quick, effective ways to tilt the glass of stress and return your life to comfort once more. It also provides you with the tools to maintain equilibrium and balance even in the most difficult times. I have included advice, techniques, and information taken from the world's ancient and modern schools of thought on relaxation, health, diet, exercise, therapy and healing. I have attempted to keep all the information as simple and as useful as possible, so that you will immediately feel the benefits.

The best way to use this book is to read through it all first and then go back to the parts that you feel are most relevant to your particular situation or circumstances.

Chapter Two is a first-aid chapter. This section offers quick, effective techniques for those who are very stressed, and provides instant comfort before you move on through the rest of the book.

Finally, I close this book by sharing with you some of my own story. I know it will show you that no matter how `down' you may get, or how badly you may be suffering, you **can** change your life (very quickly) for the better. Most importantly of all, you can maintain these changes. Know that as you work through this book, my loving support goes with you.

Chapter One

Human Beings

The one truth of this Universe is its unity.
This underlying fact of life, when known, will set you free.

Like the universe we live in, we are composed of vibrating energy. It could be said that we operate on three levels:

> a life spark - Self
> a mind or conscious awareness
> a body - the personal vehicle we inhabit

The Mind
The mind is continually at work in monitoring, gathering, storing and comparing information from the environment so that we can make decisions that keep us alive. It is also responsible for internally controlling our state of being, which enables us to survive and evolve.

The Brain
The brain is the organ of the mind, a super computer with almost unlimited capacity to receive, transmit, evaluate and record millions of pieces of information every second of our lives. Some information is made immediately available in awareness (the conscious mind); other information is kept on hold but readily available for recall (the preconscious). Everything else is dealt with by other mind functions outside our conscious awareness. This third part we call the unconscious or subconscious mind, always working outside our general awareness. We are unconscious of the complexity of its functions, but very aware of some of the effects of these functions. Without them we could not live.

The Senses

Our senses are the gateways used by the mind for collecting and transmitting information. This information can be divided into two main categories: external and internal.

External - information is gathered about where we are, what we are doing, etc.

Internal - our senses gather information about all our bodily functions, metabolism, heartbeat, blood pressure, etc.

Mind Language

Mind language contains pictures, symbols, words, sounds, smells, tastes, physical feelings and emotions. We see, hear, feel, taste and smell life, while the mind computes and interprets this information, taking any resultant action as and when required. Only need-to-know information is allowed to filter into our conscious awareness, the remainder is dealt with by the inner/unconscious processes. All useful information is stored in our memory for future reference. The mind continues this process by adding and linking experiences, and storing sensory information in the depths of memory.

Learning And Updating

The processes of learning and updating never cease, and help us to develop strategies for coping with life situations in a unique way; we are able to develop strategies for reacting to life situations. You could say, that the frame we see through, affects the picture we are viewing and consequently the way we react to it. This is why we each have individual ways of responding to stimuli.

Stress

Stress can simply be described as the demands made on each of us to adapt, cope or adjust. Some stress is healthy and necessary to keep us alert and occupied. In 1980 Hans Selye, a stress researcher, named this helpful kind of stress "Eustress".

Stress Overload

If, however, stresses are too intense, continue over too long a period, or are aimed at an over-sensitive nervous system, they can overtax that person's capacity to adjust, causing all kinds of problems. Some of these stresses occur from conditions and experiences that are threatening or harmful to a person's well-being. Others coincide with life changes. These confrontational conditions are often termed stressors, and can be positive or negative, happy or sad.

Life is full of stressors: loss of a loved one, a job, a possession; death of a loved one, or a close family member; problems at work, at school, in relationships; changes in financial status; moving home; getting married; having an accident, and many more. Stressors can pile up, and if we are unable to resolve them, it's likely that our nervous system will become clogged by negative emotions, unfulfilled desires and resultant frustrations. These blockages will lead to a less efficient nervous system.

The mind works like a complex communication network and when blockages occur, malfunctions are a likely outcome. Messages get garbled, responses become confused and chaos ensues. In the case of a human being, this internal chaos can lead to incorrect function of organs, glands and cells. The resultant mind/body confusion often causes mental and/or physical problems.

A few examples of conditions that can be stress-related are phobias, allergies, eating disorders, sexual problems, alcohol and drug abuse, anxiety, panic attacks, some forms of depression, asthma, ulcers, high or low blood pressure, some heart conditions, some skin disorders, low energy, low self-esteem and lack of confidence, stammering, behavioural problems. I could go on and on. Scientists world-wide now consider overloads of stress to be a significant factor in a large percentage of present day problems.

To live successfully, it is important that we deal effectively with each new situation as it arises. We need to identify any cause of stress and react to it in a satisfying way.

There are certain warning signs that can give you an indication that overload is imminent. These signs can include increased muscular tension, headaches, neck pain, lower back pain, teeth grinding, trembling, shaking, nervous tics and low energy. If we ignore these signs, they can eventually lead to more serious conditions such as high blood pressure, migraine, irritable bowel syndrome, indigestion and stomach disorders. Other signs may include fast pulse, hyperventilation, palpitations, sweating, fainting, dizziness and sleeping disorders.

Emotions, feelings and behaviours can also be disturbed, leading to poor concentration, anxiety, periods of worrying, irritability, lethargy and depression. Those nearing overload often also become more accident-prone.

Modern Life And Stressors
Modern life is often stressful. We change jobs, become unemployed, end marriages and relationships, travel further, and we live in an increasingly violent society. We also have access to world news and information from radio, TV and computer networks. At every moment, we are bombarded with advertising, encouraging us to spend more and get into debt. Stressors can also occur as a result of happy tensions such as babies being born, winning the lottery, going away on holiday, or starting a new relationship. These, and many others, can be very demanding.

Stressors can throw you off balance. Some stressors act internally, such as irrational worrying about anything and everything. Others act externally, such as noisy and badly polluted environments, babies crying, nagging partners or bosses.

Due to our individual history, each of us reacts to similar situations in different ways. This also applies to the way we react to stressors: they can provoke different responses in each individual. We might even react in a different way to the same stressor at a different time. Broadly speaking, it could be said that we respond to stress in one of three ways: `fight', `flight' or `flow' responses.

All of these responses work well in certain situations and none can be said to be right or wrong. But if we rely on only one of these as our general response to most tensions, we are then courting disaster.

Fight Response

This has two forms: external and internal. Users of the external form meet the problem assertively and head on, sometimes before it has time to build up. The types of people who employ this strategy tend to be energetic, ambitious and competitive - usually high achievers constantly pushing themselves to do better. They are impatient, easily irritated, and mostly intolerant of others who do not share their views. Typically these people find it hard to relax and can be at risk from heart disorders or susceptible to chronic fatigue and other degenerative disorders.

Problems can also be dealt with by the internal fight response, but people who use it appear unemotional, organised and in control, rather than outwardly aggressive. They tend to be fixed in their ways and deal stubbornly with any opposition. Unfortunately, imbalance can result in digestive disorders - irritable bowel syndrome, stomach ulcers and other internal problems.

Flight Response

People who employ this response usually avoid problems by pretending they don't exist, or by giving up. They are pleased to let others deal with them. They are over-cautious in most situations, prone to lose control of their lives, and become overly dependent on other people. These people are unlikely to live life fully or to express their feelings to others. They are often isolated, lonely and withdrawn. In extreme cases, feelings of despair can result leading to more dangerous conditions.

Flow Response

People who use this response accept stressors without fighting or running away from them. They go with the flow, letting the feelings of the moment guide them. They often appear to be vague and have no fixed values or beliefs. They have difficulty in making firm decisions or taking action. These people may feel that nothing really matters. They can be accident-prone and suffer mild illnesses. Often gullible, they can be fooled by passing health fads and fringe cults.

What Is A Human Being

As a human being you have within you a record of all you have done and all that has happened to you since you were born. If you could translate all of this action into true understanding, you would now be living a healthy, happy, relaxed, life free from illness, disorders or discomforts. But the chances are a thousand to one that you are not. For instance, what do you do if you have a headache? Most people take a headache remedy and get instant relief from the pain. Then, when comfortable at last, they give it no further thought. Very few people try to seek out the cause. Sometimes, of course, the cause is all too obvious, yet even then the tendency is to seek relief from the effect, rather than correct the cause.

Having spent your entire life with your present body, you should now know better. In most cases headaches are not necessary, and when sudden, unexpected pressures create one, you should know how to eliminate it quickly and easily, without medication. If you cannot, you do not know much about your body. You have tremendous capacities, far more and far greater than you suspect. You have taught yourself, or have been taught, certain skills in order to survive, live and even earn money. Why not use them to understand yourself?

Energy

The universe is a virtual sea of energy. All energy vibrates at different rates. Remember: our senses detect these frequencies of energy and inform our conscious mind of some of them. All scientists now agree that physical matter is made up of atoms, which are in turn composed of electrons, protons and neutrons (particles of energy moving at incredibly high speeds). Even the air we breathe and the space from here to the stars is one great sea of vibrating energy, composed of positive and negative particles. There are two kinds of energy we use: physical energy and psychic or mind energy.

Physical Energy

Our physical energy comes to us from what we eat and drink, and from the air we breathe. A small part of our psychic energy comes to us this way, but most of it comes through our psychic centres. These centres can be likened to transformers which tap into the sea of energy around us, and condition it for our use.

Psychic Energy

Psychic energy is rather like electricity, but is more subtle. Like electricity it has polarity, and this polarity can be controlled. Most of us have too much energy of negative polarity and not enough positive, and thus we are out of balance. Because of the modern world and its bombardment of stressors upon us, balance is often difficult to achieve and even more difficult to maintain.

Overbalanced Emotions

When emotions become too intense, they tend to overbalance the body to the negative side, resulting in destructive conditions and illness. Illness is sometimes our body's way of telling us that we have been doing something wrong and to stop it. We can also overbalance on the positive side, which usually results in nervous tension or mental illness. It is well to remember that the ideal is a state of equilibrium, and we should strive to achieve this.

So how can we make the necessary changes to gain or regain balance and equilibrium?

Firstly, we must understand the ways of contacting that unconscious part of our mind and enlisting its full participation and understanding of our needs and requirements. Fortunately, throughout time, many wise people have devoted their lives and resources to studying this problem, and have provided us with easy-to-use ways of enriching our lives. From the next chapter onwards, this book is dedicated to describing some of these methods, exercises and techniques which have:

- Opened effective communication between all levels of the mind.
- Offered ways of gaining deep rest and relaxation.
- Provided therapies for improving the effectiveness of the immune system.
- Given access to unlimited potential for improvements in relationships, communications, attitudes, confidence and health.
- Provided opportunities for gaining personal balance and equilibrium.

Summary

- Each person is an energy system composed of spirit, mind and body.
- The senses are channels through which we experience and gather information. They all work in frequency bands.
- Information collected through the senses is stored in the memory and added to and updated as learning. This learning helps us to live life in a more efficient manner.
- Life's functions all contain elements of stress. It is the fuel of life. But if it overloads a person's life, then problems and illness can result.
- Scientists now acknowledge that over seventy percent of all known disease is stress-related.
- Stressors are anything that can throw us off balance.
- Coping with stress is an ongoing task of effectively responding to stressors.
- The warning signs of stress overload affect the body, mind, feelings and behaviour.
- Because of our individual life histories, we each react to stressors in different ways.
- Basically, we can categorise responses into three groups: fight, flight and flow. Each of these categories has its advantages and disadvantages. Ideally a person would use a healthy blend of responses.
- Some people use one of these responses to all stressors. This can cause problems and illness.
- Each of us is a mini-universe of energy.
- We use two types of energy: physical and psychic. We obtain physical energy from the food we eat and the air we breathe. We obtain some psychic energy from food and air and most of it comes through our psychic centres. Our psychic centres are like transformers.
- Our psychic energy has positive and negative poles.
- A high concentration of emotions tends to overbalance the body on the negative side, leading to disorders.
- Some people are overbalanced on the positive side, leading to nervous or mental illness.

Chapter Two

First Aid

Peace, from inward freedom comes with goodwill to all life;
Obeying Universal Laws, free from hate and strife.

Please read this entire chapter before attempting any of the techniques.

CAUTION: Before proceeding, I must mention that all techniques and advice throughout this book are for people who are interested in improving the quality of their life and coping with the high stresses of modern living. Anyone suffering from a clinically diagnosed mental illness or psychological condition such as clinical depression or anxiety disorder, or who has any doubts about their mental state, is advised to consult their doctor and/or specialist before using any material from this book.

So how can we get the best out of life and enjoy stressful situations without our system getting overloaded with stress? Read on and I'm sure you will discover some of the answers. I presume that like myself, when you read a practical help book, you want to get some benefit right from the beginning. So here are some techniques and advice to help you begin to feel instantly more relaxed and considerably less tense.

Correct Breathing
Breathing is the most important bodily function. It should be natural and comfortable. When overstressed, most of us breathe incorrectly which can lead to further tension and self-consciousness. At such times, we are apt to keep our shoulders tight and the tummy pulled in when inhaling which prevent effective breathing. Consequently, stale air lying in the bottom of the lungs is getting more stale, whilst the body is retaining toxins which

should have been exhaled. This situation prevents sufficient oxygen getting around the blood stream, and over a period of time confusion ensues within the body/mind communication network.

Earlier we discovered that in these blocked situations the nervous system is liable to malfunction, particularly in the way the glands secrete hormones and other substances into the body. These imbalances often lead to tension, illness and disease. Of course, I'm not saying that this is the only cause of illness and discomfort, but it can certainly contribute to it. Let us now discover how, by using a few simple techniques and developing some healthy habits, we can loosen up.

The Relaxing Breath
Sit or lie down. If possible, kick off your shoes and loosen any clothing. Close your eyes. Let your body go loose and limp. Pretend that you have no bones in your body, and flop. Now check that you are completely comfortable throughout your whole body:

1. Check your head, neck, and face; let go of all the tension, and feel your muscles become elastic and loose.

2. Check that your shoulders, arms and hands are heavy and limp. Release all the tension in your tummy muscles, thighs, lower legs and feet.

3. Now quickly let your attention go all the way through your body. From the top of your head, all the way down to the tips of your toes, you are cosy and totally loose. If you should find any part that is tense, gently move that part into a more comfortable position.

4. Now, making sure that your tummy stays floppy take a gentle deep breath and fill your lungs from the bottom up. Make sure that you don't overfill your lungs.

5. Hold your breath for a count of two, and then, with your mouth slightly open, gently exhale the air.

6.   As you exhale, let your body settle down so that you are even more comfortable. Let your lungs do their job; don't interfere.

7.   Continue breathing like this for a couple of minutes. Tingling is a good sign and indicates that relaxation is taking place.

Note: Whenever you get an opportunity during your day, treat yourself to a couple of minutes of this quality breathing. Soon you will begin to breathe naturally in this way. In fact, your unconscious mind will be doing it for you.

A Sound Technique
This is a technique rather similar to the previous one, but much more powerful. This time we are going to introduce the thought of the word `calm' into the process. In this technique, we will be using the benefits of correct breathing, and the `Science of Sound'.

I will explain about the theories within the `Science of Sound' in a later chapter, together with some more advanced techniques, but because this is the first aid chapter, we will just do the technique and feel its benefits. *The proof of the pudding is in the eating.*

The Calm Routine
1.   Wrap up warmly. Sit or lie down comfortably with your eyes closed.

2.   Ensure that your head and neck are supported and your body is in its most comfortable position.

3.   Let your body slump and pretend that you have no bones in your body.

4.   Allow your tummy muscles to flop, loose and limp.

5.   Take a gentle deep breath through your nose. Do not force your breathing or over-breathe.

6.   With your mouth slightly open, exhale, thinking of the word CALM during the whole out-breath.

7. With each out-breath, allow your body to settle down more comfortably. Continue like this for a while until you feel really comfortable.

8. During this period of rest, imagine, in your mind's eye, the word CALM spelt in soothing, giant, coloured letters. You could imagine floating over the word or feeling it enter your body. Try it, it's great fun!

9. After a short while, you are likely to feel pleasant sensations of warmth, tingling or of easing in your hands, feet, chest and/or other parts of your body.

10. Continue breathing gently. Whenever you realise that you have lost the thought of the word CALM, bring it back into your mind. Don't concentrate on the word CALM, just have an awareness of it.

Note: Doing this routine twice a day for about ten to fifteen minutes, will reduce your stress levels and bring quick relief. Better health and feelings of well-being are the results.

The Calm Routine can also be used for about two or three minutes when feeling overtired, just before an interview, or as a pick-me-up at any time of the day or night. This routine is deeply relaxing, and the following suggestions will ensure that you get maximum benefits from the practice:

- Make sure your bladder is comfortable before doing *The Calm Routine.*
- Find a place where you are unlikely to be disturbed during your session.
- Make sure that you are sitting (not lying down) in a comfortable chair, and wrap up warmly.
- Make sure there are no ticking clocks or music playing during your session.
- Do this CALM routine twice daily for about 15 minutes.
- Take a few minutes rest afterwards, usually with your eyes open, before getting on with your day.

The Energiser Technique

This technique is particularly useful if you have low energy, feel lethargic, or are feeling a bit depressed. It is also good at the start of the day, or as a pick-me-up after a difficult day at work.

1. Imagine your body is an electrical battery and stores energy which may be used for specific purposes

2. Close your eyes. See the universe as an ocean of energy, and yourself as a small lake running from the ocean. Absorb some of its penetrating energy.

3. Sit down comfortably, stretch your arms out in front of you and start to shake your hands vigorously. Shake them around in any direction they want to go. Shake them faster and faster. Remember to breathe gently and deeply as you do this. At first, shaking your hands will take some effort, but as soon as you loosen both your hands and arms, the shaking will become effortless and will almost seem to happen automatically.

4. Allow your mind to feel calm and gradually let your whole body begin to shake. Soon you will feel yourself tingling with energy.

5. After a couple of minutes, let your hands drop into your lap. Sit comfortably with your body slumped and your eyes closed, breathing gently and easily, and feeling the pleasant energy tingling through you.

6. Enjoy these feelings for a few moments. Then stand up, keeping your eyes closed, and allow your whole body to vibrate. Breathe easily, loosen your body, and just move any part that seems to want to move. Eventually you might find your body makes movements of its own. That's OK. You might even feel like making dance movements; just go for it! After a few minutes, just stop. (You can stop any time you want.)

7. Now just stand there imagining that you are surrounded by tingling, sparkling light.

8.   Imagine the tingling energy in your body flowing into every part of you. You are alive with energy.

9.   Sit down and relax. Keep your tummy loose and breathe easily and deeply.

10. Now rub your hands together to make them warm. Then place your hot or warm hands on any part of your body where you are experiencing tension. Breathe gently, and imagine your hands sending the warm, healing energy into that part. Within seconds you will experience an easing and comfort.

11. Again, rub your hands together and place them on any other part that needs relaxing.

12. Do this a few more times, and then relax, breathing gently.

13. When you are ready, get up, feeling wonderfully refreshed.

Advice

In our modern civilisation we are surrounded by man-made products, fibres and materials, and massive amounts of electrical equipment. Consequently, we are saturated with static electricity. It's in our clothes, our hair, and everywhere. As our nervous system is an electrochemical organism, it's not hard to guess that this static electricity could be playing havoc with its workings. Therefore it is most important that we rid ourselves of this form of pollution.

Owning an ioniser is useful, but if you haven't yet got one, here are some other tips for you:

•   When you buy new clothes, check that they are made of natural fibre: cotton, wool, silk, etc. If not, ensure that the amount of man-made fibre contained in them is not more that twenty percent.
•   Whenever and wherever you can, take your shoes off. This allows you to earth yourself.

- Have showers in preference to baths. A shower acts as an ioniser. If you have a bath, rub your body down afterwards with a cold flannel before patting yourself dry with a cotton towel.
- Do not keep electrical appliances alongside your bed.
- Take walks near rivers, the sea or trees.
- If you get the chance, touch the bark of healthy trees with the palms of your hands as this is very energising.

Water

Next to air, water is our most precious requirement. How much pure water do you consume each day? You probably take copious amounts of polluted water in the form of coffee, tea, fizzy drinks etc.. But how much pure water does your body actually get?

We are water beings: approximately eighty percent of our body consists of water. Our cells are made of it, our blood is based on it, our organs, glands and immune system rely on it for life. Yet we only replenish it in polluted form. I advise you to go to your nearest chemist or drug store and buy a water filter jug. Drink glasses of this life-giving fluid frequently throughout the day. Replace most of your tea and coffee intake with nice, healthy glasses of water. Put it in a bottle and take it to work and instead of drinking fizzy poison, drink life-giving water. You will feel instantly healthier and more vibrant. Water is life itself. Drink it.

Air And Breathing

Air is our most important need; without it we are dead. Unfortunately, we live in a civilisation that pumps filth into our environmental air supply. People who live in towns and cities are breathing in traffic fumes and other noxious gases twenty-four hours a day. This is why I suggested that you take walks near trees or running water. Trees are nature's wonder filters and transformers. A large tree will probably consume up to fifty gallons of water from the soil each day. From this water it will extract hydrogen for its own use, and then pump out oxygen into the air around it.

Streams, rivers, seas and oceans are also filters. They absorb the filth that we create and transform it back into natural products. Therefore, for those of us who live in the midst of pollution, our best opportunity to breathe pure air is near trees and running water. A good, brisk walk for twenty minutes each day in such an environment works wonders for our body and mind.

Food And Nourishment

For a healthy diet we require, among other things, some fibre, protein and a good balance of vitamins and minerals. To obtain these, we require a daily intake of fresh vegetables, either raw or lightly cooked, and at least one piece of fruit, such as an apple or orange. As our protein intake we can have cheese, a portion of fish or poultry, beans, pulses, dairy products, eggs, and nuts.

Avoid too much red meat and animal fat; these are unhealthy if taken in too large amounts. At breakfast time, a good wholesome cereal will provide a large portion of the daily requirement of fibre. Never overeat; aim at filling no more than two thirds of your stomach then stop eating. Eat in peace and quiet if possible, and never when you are upset or angry.

Summary

In this first aid section we have learned three useful techniques:

1. *The Relaxing Breath*. This can be used several times a day for about two minutes each time. It is useful for breaking the bad habit of tense, shallow breathing.

2. *The Calm Routine*. This is a pleasant, yet very effective, way of of relaxing. Using this twice daily you will soon feel more relaxed, less stressed and more energetic. For those who are predominantly anxious and nervous, it should be used for fifteen minutes twice daily, followed by five minutes lying down with your open. For those who are more prone to feelings of lethargy and depression, it should be used for about five minutes twice daily, followed by five minutes lying down with your eyes open, and a couple of minutes of *The Energiser Technique*.

3. *The Energiser Technique*. This can be used whenever you need to feel more vibrant, or as a pick-me-up. It is especially useful for those suffering with low energy, lethargy or feelings of depression.

We have also learned that:

*   Static electricity can disrupt our natural functions.
*   It is important to earth ourselves.
*   Ionisation is beneficial to our feelings of well-being.
*   A substantial intake of fresh water is essential to good health.
*   Air is our most vital commodity. The best places to breathe pure air are near trees and/or rivers, streams, waterfalls, seas, and oceans.
*   Daily exercise helps to keep the body toned and the mind relaxed.

Chapter Three

Breath Is Life

"The Lord God formed the man from the dust of the ground and breathed into his nostrils the breath of life, and the man became a living being." Genesis 2:7

Life is absolutely dependent upon the act of breathing. This is a fundamental principle.

To breathe is to live, and without breath there is no life. Every creature and life-form on this planet needs a supply of air for survival; even plants cannot exist without it. In humans, breathing may be considered the most important of all the functions of the body. We may exist for some time without eating, a shorter time without drinking, but without breathing our existence may be measured by a few minutes. Not only are we dependent upon breath for life, but we are largely dependent upon correct habits of breathing for continued vitality and freedom from tension and illness. An informed control of our breathing power will lengthen our days upon the earth, by giving us increased vitality and powers of resistance to disease. On the other hand, careless breathing will tend to shorten life by decreasing vitality and making us prone to disease.

In a normal state, we breathe easily and as nature intended, but most of us exist in a hectic, modern environment where natural habits are altered and distorted. It is not only our breathing that is affected in this way: our attitudes of walking, standing and sitting may also be filled with tension which in turn further effect our breathing patterns. The percentage of civilised people who breathe correctly is quite small, and the result of incorrect breathing is shown in contracted chests, stooping shoulders, and terrible increases in asthma and other respiratory disorders even among the very young.

In Western society, it is widely accepted that physical health depends upon correct breathing and good air quality. The Ageless Wisdom of the East teaches us that in addition to the physical benefit derived from correct habits of breathing, our mental power, happiness, self-control, clear-sightedness, morals and even spiritual growth may be increased by an understanding of the `Science of Breath'. Whole schools of Oriental philosophy have been founded upon this science.

When we breathe, we draw the air in through the nose, where it is warmed by contact with the mucous membranes. These membranes are plentifully supplied with blood. The air then passes through the pharynx and larynx into the windpipe (trachea), which divides into the two bronchi, which in turn subdivide into the bronchial tubes (bronchia), the bronchioles and eventually into millions of little air sacs (alveoli). It then flows into the millions of tiny blood vessels, or capillaries, which surround the tiny air sacs in the lungs. Air is drawn into our lungs by the action of the diaphragm. This is a large muscle stretched like a sheet across the lower chest, separating the chest cavity from the abdomen. The diaphragm's action is usually involuntary as is that of the heart. It can also, however, be operated voluntarily. The diaphragm is drawn downwards which creates a vacuum. This vacuum draws air into the lungs and the chest cavity expands. When the diaphragm contracts, it moves upwards so reducing the space within the chest cavity, which compresses the lungs and so air is expelled.

When our blood starts out on its journey from the lungs, it is bright red and rich, full of life-giving oxygen and nourishment. It then returns poor, blue, dull, and laden with waste matter from our system. This blood then goes to the right auricle of the heart. As soon as it is full, the auricle contracts and forces the stream of blood into the right ventricle, out through the pulmonary artery to the lungs. It then flows into the millions of capillaries which surround the tiny air sacs in the lungs.

As a breath is inhaled an exchange happens. The walls of the capillaries carrying the waste-laden blood back to the lungs contain tiny holes big enough for air to pass through but too small to let blood through. When the oxygen from an inhaled breath comes into contact with the blood through the capillary walls, a form of combustion takes place, and the blood gives up the waste gases in exchange for oxygen. In this way the blood is purified and oxygenated. It returns to the left auricle of the heart, is forced into the left ventricle, and is again pumped out through the arteries on its life-giving mission. It has been estimated that in every twenty-four hours, thirty-five thousand pints of blood will have traversed the capillaries of your lungs.

I hope that you are now able to realise how important it is for you to breathe in sufficient quantities of fresh air and also how important it is that you effectively exhale the impure air from your lungs.

The `Science Of Breath'

The `Science of Breath' teaches that breathing occurs not only to oxygenate the system, but also to aid absorption of the prana-vital force into the nervous system. Before proceeding further let us take a hasty glance at the nervous system.

The Nervous System

This is divided into two great systems: the cerebrospinal system and the sympathetic system.

The Cerebrospinal System

This system attends to all seeing, hearing, tasting, smelling, feeling, etc.. It sets is used by the mind to think (to manifest consciousness) and is the instrument by which the mind communicates with the outside world. This system may be likened to a communications system, with the brain as the central office and the spinal column and nerves as cables and channels.

The brain is a great mass of nerve tissue. It consists of three parts: the cerebrum or main brain (made up of two cerebral hemispheres), the cerebellum, and the medulla oblongata or brain stem..

The cerebrum occupies the upper, front, middle and back portion of the skull and deals with intellectual action. The cerebellum, or `little brain', fills the lower and back portion of the skull. It regulates the movements of the voluntary muscles. The medulla oblongata is the broadened commencement of the spinal cord, lying below and in front of the cerebellum. It is the upper, enlarged end of the spine, and, from this, branch forth the cerebrum. These reach to various parts of the head, to the organs of special sense, to some of the thoracic and abdominal organs, and to the organs of respiration. The spinal cord runs down the spinal canal in the vertebral column. It is a long mass of nerve tissue, branching off at several vertebrae to nerves communicating with all parts of the body. It is like a large telephone cable, and the nerves are like the private wires connecting with their own parts.

The Sympathetic Nervous System
This consists of a double chain of ganglia - a mass of nervous matter including nerve cells, on the sides of the spinal column - and scattered ganglia in the head, neck, chest and abdomen. These ganglia are connected with each other by filaments, and are also connected with the cerebrospinal system by motor and sensory nerves. From these ganglia, numerous fibres branch out to the organs of the body, blood vessels, etc. At various points, the nerves meet together and form what are known as plexuses. The sympathetic system practically controls the involuntary processes, such as circulation, respiration and digestion.

The power or force transmitted via the nerves from the brain to all parts of the body is known as nerve force. In character and rapidity it resembles an electric current. Without this nerve force the heart cannot beat, the blood cannot circulate, the lungs cannot breathe, the various organs cannot function; in fact the machinery of the body would come to a stop. The brain itself cannot think without nerve force being present. When you realise this, it is easy to see the importance of the absorption of nerve force.

The `Science of Breath' teachings include important information about the solar plexus. This is a really important part of the nervous system and is recognised as a form of "abdominal brain". It is situated in the epigastric region, just behind the `pit of the stomach' on either side of the spinal column. It is composed of white and grey nerve tissue, and is said to store vital force. It radiates strength and energy to all parts of the body.

Nostril Breathing vs Mouth Breathing

We are designed so that we can take air in through either the nose or the mouth. By far the healthiest way to breathe is through the nose, as it acts as a natural filter. It contains two nostrils - narrow channels filled with bristly hairs - which filter, strain and sieve the air of some of its impurities. These impurities are then expelled when the breath is exhaled. Each nostril is lined by mucous membrane which warms the incoming air, thus preventing it from damaging the delicate organs of the throat and lungs. If the nose becomes cluttered with too many impurities, it causes us to sneeze, which removes them.

Mouth breathing, on the other hand, allows vast amounts of cold, impure air to enter the throat and lungs. It also allows the nasal passages to become clogged and unclean through lack of use. Those who habitually breathe through the nose are not likely to be troubled with clogged or stuffy nostrils, but mouth breathers risk throat and chest infections.

Categories Of Respiration

Breathing can be roughly classified into three categories. These are:

High Breathing

This is often known as clavicular, or collarbone, breathing. Breathing in this way elevates the ribs and raises the collarbone and shoulders, at the same time drawing the tummy in. Only the upper part of the chest and lungs are used, and consequently only a small amount of air is allowed to enter. Stale air remains in the lower part of the lungs and impurities are not properly evacuated from the body. This is probably the most unhealthy form of breathing and can lead to disease and lung problems.

Mid Breathing

Mid breathing is sometimes called intercostal breathing. Whilst not as inefficient as high breathing, this category of breathing still leaves a lot to be desired. When you breathe in this way, the ribs are raised and the chest is partially expanded.

Low Breathing

Abdominal breathing is a good way of taking in reasonable quantities of air and expelling impurities from the lungs. The tummy muscles are left loose and, as air is breathed in, the tummy expands, allowing the lungs to almost fill. Noxious gases are then expelled when the air is exhaled.

Breathing For Health And Vitality

By understanding the principles of breathing, the Oriental Masters evolved practices, techniques and exercises capable of producing healthy condition. Here follow some of the most useful practices:

The Complete Breath

This technique of breathing makes full use of the lungs and consequently improves the quality of your blood, complexion, appearance and general health. It also aids in alertness and clarity of mind. You should take a few complete breaths whenever you can during the day. Try to ensure that you are in an area where the air quality is good. (Ideal times to do this technique are morning and evening, and it can also be done at any other time, every day. It is also the basis for other breathing techniques.)

How to do *The Complete Breath*:

1. Sit comfortably and breathe normally.

2. Gently push your tummy out as you inhale, filling the bottom of the lung and slowly counting 1, 2, 3.

3. Pull your tummy in as you continue filling the centre of the lung counting 4, 5, 6.

4. Finally raise your shoulders still breathing in and counting 7, 8, 9.

5. Now hold the air in your lungs for the count of 6.

6. Breathe out for the count of 9, allowing your body to return to its original position.

7. When the lungs are empty, repeat this breathing at least another four times.

Some points worth noting when practising this exercise:

*   Learn to make the three physical movements of the inhalation flow smoothly into one another.
*   The inhalation is continuous; do not stop the inhalation until the lungs have been completely filled during the 9-second count.
*   Inhale and exhale in a very controlled manner so that you cannot hear the air going in or coming out of the nostrils.
*   All breathing is done through the nose.
*   Make sure that the air is completely exhaled and your lungs are as empty as possible before you begin your next inhalation. Contract your stomach at the end of the exhalation to ensure that the lungs are empty.
*   Close your eyes throughout the exercise and count all movements carefully.
*   After some practice, you might consider extending your count as follows: bottom lungs: 1, 2, 3, 4, 5, mid-lung: 6, 7, 8, 9, 10, raised shoulders: 11, 12, 13, 14, 15. Hold the air in the lungs for 10. Exhale for 15.

The Cleansing Breath

This breathing technique is useful for ventilating and cleansing the lungs. It stimulates the cells and gives a general tone to the respiratory organs. It also helps to develop the vocal chords and keep the throat muscles toned up. (Ideal times to use this technique are when first arising in the morning and when getting home from work in the evening.)

1. Inhale a complete, deep breath.

2. Hold the air in the lungs for a few seconds.

3. Pucker up the lips as if to whistle, but do not swell out the cheeks.

4. Now exhale a short burst of air through the mouth.

5. Stop again, holding the air.

6. Now exhale another short burst from the mouth.

7. Continue with these short bursts of out-breath, until the lungs are empty.

8. Repeat this two or three more times, then rest.

The Invigorating Breath

This technique is designed to stimulate and invigorate the nervous system, and increase feelings of well-being and vitality. (The ideal time to do the technique is as a pick-me-up or just before doing anything that requires concentration.)

1. Stand up straight without tension.

2. Inhale a complete breath, and hold.

3. Extend the arms straight out in front of you, without any strain.

4. Slowly draw the hands back towards the shoulders, gradually tightening the muscles and clenching the fists.

5. Then keeping the muscles tense, push the fists slowly out in front of you again and then back rapidly to the shoulders. Repeat this procedure a few more times.

6. Now exhale vigorously through the mouth.

7. Relax, and then repeat this another four times, resting between each round.

8. On completion, rest for a few minutes so that your body can assimilate the full benefits of the technique.

The Balanced Breath
This technique need only take about one to two minutes to complete. It offers immediate relaxation and release from stress. (Use at any time to relax or to calm yourself.)

1. Find a comfortable chair.

2. Sit upright with your spine straight and both feet on the floor: don't lounge.

3. Close your eyes.

4. Gently close the right nostril with the thumb of your right hand and slowly breath out through your left nostril. Then inhale easily through the same left nostril.

5. Close the left nostril with the two middle fingers of your right hand and breath out of the right nostril. Inhale easily through the same right nostril.

6. Continue alternating breaths in this way for about one or two minutes, or until you feel very relaxed. Never do this for more than five minutes at any one time.

Points worth noting when practising *The Balancing Breath*:

*   It is advisable to blow your nose before commencing this exercise.
*   Each time you breathe, always breathe out first and then in through the same nostril.
*   Do not count or time your breaths; just allow yourself to feel comfortable whether breathing in or out.
*   Do not hold your breath between breaths.
*   Never strain or over-breathe.
*   Breathe gently and silently.
*   Each time you breathe out, allow your body to become more loose and limp.
*   Don't rush to get up after the exercise. Take a few moments to become fully alert.
*   Always finish the exercise breathing out of the left nostril with the right nostril blocked with the thumb (the same way your commenced the exercise).

Summary

- Breath is life; without it, we are dead.
- In the East, it is recognised that correct breathing leads not only to good physical health but also happiness, clear-sightedness, and good mental health.
- The lungs and heart work together to ventilate the body and remove impurities, via the blood, through the breathing process.
- The `Science of Breath' teaches us that breathing not only oxygenates the body but also takes in vital force from the universe.
- Vital force is life enhancing and acts like a subtle form of electricity throughout the nervous system.
- The solar plexus is a very important part of the nervous system. It could be called the abdominal brain. It contains white and grey brain type, and is said to store nerve force.
- Breathing can be roughly classified into three categories and not one of them on its own is fully efficient. The three common categories of breathing are high, mid, and low breathing. Low breathing is considered to be the most efficient.
- There are four breathing techniques that can help to increase good health and vitality. *The Complete Breath* for better general health; *The Cleansing Breath* tones up respiratory organs; *The Invigorating Breath* stimulates the nervous system; *The Balancing Breath* reduces stress levels and helps with relaxation.

Chapter Four

Successful Mind Communication

Happiness; a timeless joy, this experience must be shared,
Beyond fear and excitation; flowing freely unimpaired.

The Unconscious Level Of Mind

Your unconscious mind is capable of making life easier and more fulfilling for you. In addition to operating the nervous system and keeping all the bodily processes and mechanisms working smoothly, it also takes over and makes easy the functions that are tiring and difficult at the conscious level. If your conscious mind and your unconscious mind communicate correctly, it can lead to unlimited success in all you do. However, your unconscious mind takes everything you say or think literally, and only works in the present.

If you drive a car, you no doubt can remember how difficult it was to learn everything you needed to do just to get your car moving. After repetitive practice, things eventually became much easier. Probably now you can drive without even realising all the functions you perform throughout your journey. This is because your unconscious mind has assumed the responsibility for running the whole process from a deeper level.

Learning

Learning is usually accomplished by doing something over and over again so that the unconscious can assimilate and take over the process without any conscious complications. We learn most things in this way, comfortable and uncomfortable, positive and negative. Confidence, self-esteem and successful attitudes can be understood as learning, as can phobias, anxieties, depressions, worrying and other disorders. The mind has been conditioned through repetition to almost automatically access these states.

Being able to communicate clearly with the unconscious mind can be very useful in ensuring that any future learnings are acceptable and beneficial. Proper communication can also be useful in unlearning bad, negative and painful behaviours and habits.

I have found the following communication tips to be useful in improving my own life and in helping others to gain new and healthy ways of thinking and being.

The Past - anything that has happened.
Refer to past events using past-tense language (especially traumatic or negative events). For example:

I did	*I was*	*I had*	*It was*
We were	*I felt*	*I thought*	*I went*
Those were	*Last night*	*Yesterday*	*Before*

The Present - anything that I am now experiencing.
Refer to present personal experiences using present tense, first person. For example:

I am feeling, doing, working.   *I have, I go, I work*

Refer to present happenings using the present tense. For example:

It is	*They breathe*	*We have*
They are feeling	*He is looking healthy*	

Future Goals - anything that I want to happen in my life.
Use present tense for things that you want to happen in your life. For example:
I am becoming better and more confident.
Now I am making improvements in my health.
Every second, hour, minute and day, I am feeling more and more comfortable, happier, more energetic etc..

Taboos - words or phrases in the future tense. (Remember the unconscious only acknowledges the future when it becomes the present.) Also avoid using the following when goal setting:

I should - to the unconscious this means: *I know it's right but I'm not doing it.*

I want - to the unconscious this means: *I want to want.* (In other words I will always want but never get.)

I can't - to the unconscious this means: *I have given up before I even start.*

To successfully work towards your goals, apply the above advice when speaking, thinking or writing. In this way you can turn your world around and soon effect the changes that you desire. The above understandings can also be employed within creative visualisation and affirmation techniques.

Creative Visualisation And Affirmation For Change

Simply by making a tiny adjustment in your attitude, you can change the whole direction of your life. Take, for example, someone who is very shy and inhibited. This person might find it extremely difficult to socialise. They may at times appear to enjoy being alone, but in fact detest solitude. Perhaps they would love to have a group of friends, but know that their shyness prevents the necessary communication. Were they to accept an invitation, this difference in attitude could easily alter their whole life. Breaking away and moving on from old patterns always involves a step into the unknown.

Inner sight or visualisation can immediately change you in a creative way. By changing thoughts and focusing on them, you create a cycle. The change is created by the action you are taking. Changes always happen in the now, in the present. One great benefit of creative visualisation is that if you have inner doubts and fears about something, the fact that you actually visualise things happening in new ways becomes a signal to your unconscious mind that you are open and ready. It is just like planting a seed: soon it will germinate and grow.

You now have a powerful tool to change your life in any way that you want. What you desire at deep levels is what you attract. Every day you attract and repel millions of vibrations from around you. Using visualisation helps you to attract into your life the things that you want and need. You can even find out what you desire.

Sit down somewhere comfortable. Spend a couple of minutes doing The Calm Routine. Allow your mind to settle. Now think about your life and your present situation. Think of something, anything that you would like to change or to have or do differently. Don't hold anything back, just daydream for a while and give your imagination a free reign. Just go along with your thoughts. After a few moments you will probably have decided on something. When you have done this, imagine what changes, if any, are required. Try to see in your mind's eye a picture of how you would like it to be. Be sure it will happen. Take all the time you need and when you have finished, relax. Now be sure that this is exactly what you want. Look to a successful ending and now see the way things will change through time until then. Make notes of what you will need to do and change to arrive at that successful outcome.

Types Of Visualisation
Visualisation is a general term for all internal sensing. Many of us can actually see symbols and pictures of things in our mind's eye. Vision is the most common internal sensory experience, and we may also sense sounds, tastes, smells and textures. Some people find difficulties with internal sensing and can only *think* of things. For these people, thinking is their way of visualising. Affirmations could be called *word visualisation*. For thinkers, affirmations offer a powerful alternative to visualisation techniques.

Affirmations
An affirmation is a way of 'making firm'. They can be written down or spoken. A simple example of a constructive affirmation could be *"I now attract success"* or *"I now welcome more employment opportunities"*. It is important to have a genuine desire to receive what you have asked for. After writing your affirmation, say it quietly to yourself and then speak it out loud. Always bear in mind, however, the simple rules for working with the unconscious mentioned earlier in this chapter.

Prior to doing creative visualisation and/or affirmations, first decide what goal or goals you wish to realise. Then give your intent/will a form. With visualisation this is usually an image. With affirmation, it is putting into words what we want to happen. Repetition adds power with both forms of mind work.

Using Visualisations And Affirmations Together

As well as being used separately, visualisations and affirmations can be used together. Often a great way to give more power to a visualisation is by adding an appropriate affirmation at the end or at the beginning. For instance, when visualising yourself in your new home, you could use the affirmation:

I now own this beautiful home.

Or perhaps,

I now have an abundance of money, more than enough to buy this splendid abode.
I have paid for this house.

Tenses

Most authorities on visualisation and affirmation say we should do both in the present tense, as though what we are thinking about already exists. For example, if we are going for an interview in four days time, we could affirm:

In four days' I am having a successful interview and I am accepted for that post.

The next day we could affirm:

In two days time I am feeling so confident that I am accepted for the job.

The next day:

Tomorrow I am taken on.

On the morning of the interview:

I now feel confident, relaxed and able to enjoy the interview, knowing that I have every chance of getting the job.

Using these wonderful tools for progress and improvement can create great benefits in our lives. However, it is important to remember that life must be healthy and flowing. Often the best visualisations are for goals that are right for us, but, due to blockages, we have not, so far, been able to attain them. The visualisations and affirmations help to remove some of these blocks and allow us to develop our true potential.

Standing Still

Occasionally, when using these techniques, you may come across a period when nothing seems to be happening. Sometimes this is a time of inner processing. However, if this continues for some time, you might have hit a blockage. Blockages occur when parts of you within cannot agree on an outcome. If this happens, here is a simple way to get the ball rolling once more.

Undoing Blocks

Get two pieces of paper and a pencil or pen. Now loosen up for a couple of minutes using *The Calm Routine*. Go over your goal in your mind, asking yourself what it is about this goal that seems unobtainable. Write down any negative attitudes or patterns that stand in the way of reaching your goal. Take your time doing this; jot everything down, however trivial it may seem. When you have finished putting your blockages on paper, read them through. Feel how useless they are. Now decide to destroy them. You may tear up the paper or burn it. Whatever you decide upon will be right for you. As the paper is destroyed, breathe out all your negative feelings.

On a second piece of paper, note all your positive feelings and patterns. Now write down your goal and all the reasons you can think of as to why you will achieve it. It might be useful to also add a powerful affirmation such as:

> *I am totally committed to achieving this goal. I let go of past, negative effects. I am totally open to the new.*

The best times for this work are just before going to sleep, just after waking and after a nice relaxation period. I have found that the amount of time spent on the visualisations and affirmations during these periods varies from person to person. Use common sense. For the greatest chance of success, it is good to cultivate an attitude of confident believing, yet at the same time not being too attached to the result. Just take a few minutes each day to affirm your required outcome. During the rest of the day, I suggest forget and let go of your visualisation. At the end of each period, imagine your visualisation/affirmation going off into distant space and disappearing, then forget all about it until the next time. Repeat this routine, once or twice everyday.

Your Attitude And Beliefs

Your attitude during visualisation and affirmation is vital. Remember you are sending out vibrations. The clearer and stronger the pulses are, the greater the opportunities for creativity. Thoughts and emotions all count towards your success or failure.

Beliefs are also very important; you have to believe, indeed to have conviction, that you want and need what you aim to achieve. If you are not truly open to receiving something, you don't really want it. Often part of you wants it and another part does not. To overcome this, it can be very helpful to look at your acceptance as something separate. Remember the more positive you are, the greater your chances of success.

Acceptance

If you truly desire something enough, you need to be open and ready to receive it. Be sure to deal with doubts if and when they occur. Perhaps add another affirmation, something like:

I let go of all feelings of doubt, I am open and ready, and deserve my present goal.

Examples Of Affirmations

Affirmations can be used for setting and achieving goals in many different parts of your life. You can word your own personal ones. Here are a few examples:

Relationships

Every day my relationship is getting better and more satisfying.

I now attract my perfect partner into my life.

I am open to receive and give love to my ideal person.

Love

I attract love and happiness into my life.

I now give and receive love.

Life is full of love.

Money

Every moment I am becoming richer.

I now tune in to the unlimited universal source of good fortune.

I attract incredible wealth into my life.

Health

I am becoming more and more healthier each day.

The healing power of love fills my life.

I am naturally strong and healthy.

Profession/Career

I am successful in my work.

I am ready for a change of job and now attract a perfect offer of work into my life.

Life shows me the way to successful promotion.

Goals

We have, so far, discussed ways of using visualisation and affirmation for changing and working towards achieving things. These things or outcomes are goals. Goals can therefore be described as things that you now want to achieve or possess.

Any goal you set, work towards and eventually achieve is likely to effect every part of your life. A simple scenario might be that you are looking for employment. You might need to do some training, gain a qualification, locate a vacancy, make an application, attend an interview. This will require time, travelling and expenditure. If you are in a relationship, this will effect your partner who will have less time with you, and might need to help to budget for the travelling expenses, postage, and perhaps money for new clothes to attend the interviews in. Of course, if you get the post, it's possible that your financial status could improve. If, however, you are not accepted, you will have to continue the search. You might have to do further training. At times you might feel that you are getting nowhere and get depressed or despondent. Your partner could feel these emotional changes and this is likely to have some effect on your relationship.

From the simple example above, it is obvious that any goal must be thought through carefully from every angle before a commitment to achieving it is made.

Short, Medium And Long-Term Goals

Goals can roughly be identified into three time periods or terms. These are short-term, medium-term and long-term. To be fully effective, each set should lead on to the next. The periods for each term will vary from person to person.

For this example, we will say that short-term would include things that you are working towards achieving within the next couple of months. The medium-term would be from two months to one year. Long-term might be one to five years. I have found it useful to first look at what you imagine your goal(s) might be. Then have a look at short-term actions and see if you are doing anything that might point you in that direction. Once these two groupings are identified, you can map in medium-term goals that themselves lead from short goals to your projected long-term aims.

It is well to realise at this stage that medium-term and long-term goals are best left reasonably loose, because as time goes on it is likely that adjustments and changes of direction could occur.

The next thing to do is to get these ideas clearly written down. Ask yourself the following questions and any others that come to mind and then jot down the answers:

- What qualities and strengths do I possess that will help me to achieve these goals?
- What are my weaknesses and what can I do about them?
- Do I have a burning emotional desire, a conviction or some compulsion to achieve these goals?
- Am I prepared to make the sacrifices needed to attain these desires?
- Do I have a plan of action? (It is no good just dreaming and hoping for things to happen.)
- Am I prepared to change direction and adjust my goals if I come to a dead-end?
- Do I have the backing of any significant others?
- What, at present, stands in my way and what can I do about it?
- What advantages to my life will I have when I have reached my goals?

Note: If most of the answers to these questions are in the affirmative, and you have specific, realistic answers for the others, then you may be certain that you have a very good chance of success.

Moving Forward Towards Goals
Now that you have decided what you want, you must take every opportunity to carry out the actions that you feel sure will carry you towards success. To empower these actions and to attract into your life the energies and assistance you need, you can employ the techniques of creative visualisation and affirmation discussed previously.

The Goal Chart

A more advanced way of utilising the skills of creative visualisation and affirmation is to create a goal chart.

To build this chart you will require:

- A large piece of coloured or white card. Choose a colour that you feel comfortable with.
- A set of coloured felt-tips, crayons or pens.
- Some cut-out photographs and/or pictures which a represent of your goal. For example, if your goal is to own a home, perhaps choose pictures of a nice house and some interior shots of well-furnished rooms. If it is money you are interested in, you could draw some gold coins or even stick a cheque made out to yourself for the amount that you wish to get.

Seven Factors For Successful Chart Work

There are seven interesting factors that, if applied when constructing and using a chart, may add to its effectiveness in helping you fulfil your dreams. They are:

Availability, limitation, binding, transformation, emotion, reversal, and construction.

Availability

This means that if you are going to set goals, they should be realistic enough to be achievable and not way out of reach. For example, if you are at present drawing dole, a short-term goal could be to gain training for a job, perhaps followed by a medium-term goal of being offered employment in a job that demands a good salary. The long-term goal might be to gain promotion or be well-off. An unrealistic goal at this stage would be to want to be the Chairman of the Bank of England. Who knows, at a later time maybe even that goal might be available, but before realising it you would need to put in many years of hard work. So remember, the first rule is: *always choose realistic goals, however ambitious.*

Limitation

Energy is dynamic and moving. The mind is a pool of energy. If you throw a brick into a pool it creates ripples, waves and currents which spread out in all directions. The power generated and the distance travelled by the ripples and waves rely entirely upon the size of the brick, how forcefully you throw it, and the size of the pool. Desires and the thoughts that they generate can be likened to that brick.

The mind is there to process our thoughts, and then give the necessary momentum to realise our desires in the physical world. For example, a good architect would need to have an inner vision of a structure before designing a completed building. If limits were not placed on his vision, the building could be disastrous and the construction costs would far exceed the budget given. So when we decide on a goal, it is important that we limit our vision and affirmation to exactly what we require. This limiting will keep the energy and motion within our requirements. Going back to the pool metaphor, we could use a smaller brick and throw it in the part of the pool where we wish ripples to radiate from. The architect could first find out the budget allocated for the building, its purpose and use, and what materials are needed for its construction. For example, if we were making a chart for buying a house, we could include the statement:

The home I will acquire will be within the price bracket of £80,000 - £100,000.

Binding

One of the laws of motion states that for every force in nature there is an equal and opposite force in operation. This law can also be applied to our thoughts. Therefore, when using visualisation or affirmation for anything big, it is always wise to bind the opposite force. To do this, draw a complete border or frame around the outer edge of your chart, and add to your limitation statement something like::

I also desire that when I achieve my goal, I enjoy its positive benefits for as long as I need them, without any reversal taking place.

Transformation Interface

Earlier we mentioned that the mind uses pictures, symbols, sounds, smell, tastes and feelings, including emotions internally and externally. The unconscious mind uses feelings and sensations, whilst the conscious mind uses words. Imagine that between the two there is a kind of filter-transformation interface, where words can move feelings and sensations, and where feelings and sensations can be described in words. In the average person, this filter needs to be able to transform, or step energy up or down as necessary. If this didn't happen, we would likely become an emotional mess. We could, therefore, say that words are the language of the conscious mind, and feelings and sensations are the language of the unconscious mind. We earlier concluded that many of the troubles we experience within our lives could be caused by the inability of the two minds to talk to each other. This transformation interface, if used properly, might become a cushion. When words hit it from the conscious mind, they are absorbed and then filtered through into the unconscious as emotions. Conversely, imagine emotions coming up to the inside of the mind interface, hitting it, sinking into it, passing through it, and emerging in the conscious mind as words.

Using the language of the unconscious and being aware of this imaginary transformation gate will help you use creative visualisation, affirmation and chartwork in a more productive and sensitive way.

Emotion
e - energy
motion - movement

Emotion is part of your being, the real you. In creative visualisation we are interested in generating new creative emotions. Desires are driven by emotion. Jesus said,

> "..., if you have faith as small as a mustard seed, you can say to this mountain, `Move from here to there' and it will move." Matthew 17:20

Fill your chart with pictures of things that you desire and feast your eyes on them frequently. Allow the feelings of pleasure and enjoyment to flood through your being. This is one way of using emotions productively.

Reversal

A very interesting fact is that the left-hand side of the brain works on the right-hand side of our body, and the right-hand side of the brain works on the left-hand side of our body. Some students of mysticism say that there is evidence that the next inner plane is reversed to this one. Let us say that on our physical plane we plan to go out for a walk. We begin by walking from our house down the road. We turn right at the junction and then walk along a path into the forest. We pass through the forest and enter a meadow, then sit down on a bench. Now if there is such a thing as going for a walk on the astral plain, we would start by spending some time enjoying sitting on a bench in a meadow. Then we would get up and walk out of the meadow into the forest. We would come out of the forest down a path and turn left into our street and finally reach home. Now in view of this reversal process can you see why you start out getting something by feeling that you already have it?

Construction

Now it is time to build your chart. Get your piece of card about twenty inches wide by twenty inches high. You should do this work on your own and keep your chart in a private place. It should not be in a place where others can look at it without your permission. Keep it very private. Draw a boundary line all the way around the edge of the chart. Remember, everything that you have in the material world has a representation somewhere deep inside you, so as you are creating your physical chart there is a mental counterpart being constructed within your inner mind. Remember the law of limitation that I mentioned earlier, this boundary line reinforces that limitation.

Hopefully by now you will have collected and selected stimulating colourful pictures, ones that fire up your imagination and represent your goals and desires. Next affix your pictures and drawings onto your card. Give each representation space and write affirmations and relevant comments underneath each picture or symbol.

When you are satisfied with your chart put it up on a wall in a private place. Look at it daily. The best times are usually the same as for creative visualisation and affirmation - when first waking, just before going to bed or after a nice deep relaxation period. These regular looks at your chart, while being aware of your affirmations, can bring the openings in your life for fulfilment of your desires.

After a few days or weeks, you should be able to recall the pictures and images very easily. Once you recall these pictures, you can manipulate them to suit yourself. As time goes by, you can imagine yourself in the goal chart. This projection can further stir your inner creative powers and stimulate greater activity in getting what you want.

Remember, all the finest things in the world can come to you but first they have to come through the laws of the physical plane. This takes time. One thing is sure: these things have to come to you through an increased sphere of availability. You have to give this sphere of availability a chance to grow, time to build up and increase.

Summary

- The unconscious mind always works in the present. It runs and controls your nervous system and all life-giving functions. It has access to all your memories. It monitors, communicates and operates through your senses and emotions.
- When communicated with effectively, it assists in making your life easier and more fulfilling.
- The unconscious learns by repetition. Some learned functions can be uncomfortable and negative, like phobias, anxieties, depressions, etc.. Some can be comfortable and positive, like self-confidence, successful attitudes, etc..
- You can help to change negative learning and develop more positive behaviours by using simple communication techniques to work with your unconscious processes.
- Your unconscious mind works in the present and responds to messages passed through the senses.
- Techniques using visualisation and affirmation are very effective for change work. They can be used separately or together.
- Attitude, belief and acceptance are important parts of successful mind work.
- Affirmations are best when made in the present tense with conviction and emotion.
- Statements like `I should', `I want' and `I can't' are to be avoided when goal setting.
- Goals are things we desire to achieve, usually within time limits. They can be short; medium; and long-term. Before setting goals, it is wise to be aware of consequences of achieving them.
- Once we have set goals, we must take every opportunity to carry out the actions which lead towards them.
- Building and using a goal chart can lead to realising our goals.
- There are seven main factors involved in chart work: availability, limitation, binding, transformation, emotion, reversal and construction.
- By looking at the chart daily and saying the affirmations out loud, we can stimulate our inner creative powers. This can lead to more effective goal realisation.

Chapter Five

Human Constitution

At the dawning of the Cosmos, first Law sprang into being.
To give harmony and equilibrium in everything, all seeing.
Seeded by vibration, in thought; in word; in deed;
unemotional; just; attentive; unchecked chaos to impede.

In the Ancient Eastern world, the *Rishis* (or Seers) devoted much time and study to nature and the laws of balance and excellence. They also delved into the secrets of the nature and constitution of mankind. The knowledge they obtained was then passed down from generation to generation. About 4,000 years ago, it was collected into the great books of knowledge, the *Vedas*. I consider this knowledge to be as important today as it was long ago. In fact, many of the techniques, treatments, and use of herbs, found in the *Vedas* are now becoming more available to Western societies. Today's physicians tend to ignore individuality and they often look at people as kidneys or bowels, and neglect the organism that is host to those organs. Most of today's doctors fail to project *health* onto their patients.

We all exist as individuals against the background of Mother Nature. Nobody is wholly individual, because it is nature that conditions our individuality. Most of us overindulge ourselves, relying on the world to supply everything to us, and hoping that our bodies will provide us with enough digestive power to consume whatever we take in.

The Meaning Of Life
Life is meant to be pleasurable, but overindulgence takes the sharpness out of living. We lose your ability to enjoy if we continually exceed our limits. Limitation is part of our inheritance, and is reflected in dozens of life's transactions. These include the

necessity to breathe, eat, sleep and communicate with others. Our most important limitation is our organism's capacity to endure our indulgences. Either we willingly limit ourself or Mother Nature will limit you. Birgit Heyn (1987) says,

"Every wrong use or non-use of the senses leads to a disharmony in humans, and the disharmonies between human beings and nature."

Nature is not there to kill us, but to protect and warn us of our errors. If we ignore these warnings, things can get very serious.

Four Essential Life Goals

The Ancient Masters considered that in order to live in a fulfilling manner, it is important to work through the following four goals:

Dharma:	Fulfilling our duty as a citizen or member of a group, tribe etc..
Artha:	Earning a living and gaining possessions.
Kama:	Using possessions to help us progress through life
Moksha:	Comprehending life as more than the other three goals.

Existence

To help you understand the theories behind this ancient knowledge, here is a very brief outline of the model of human existence. Everything is formed from energy and matter. The Ancient Masters speculated that for matter to come into being, it required three primary qualities. These they called *Gunas:*

Sattva:	Balance, existence, essence, being, true life, light.
Rajas:	Activity, emotion, feeling, passion.
Tamas:	Inertia, lethargy, darkness, solidness.

From these primary qualities came the five Great Elements:

Earth:	Solid matter. Its characteristic is stability.
Ether:	Space. The distance between things.
Water:	Liquid acts as a flux.
Fire:	A transformational power. It has form but not substance.
Air:	Dynamic, moving gas.

The Three Doshas-Force

The five Great Elements are reconciled, facilitated, and coaxed into co-operative alliances by the three principle Doshas. These are Vata, Pitta and Kapha. Vata operates within Ether and Air; Pitta works with Fire and Water; and Kapha is the Dosha of Earth and Water. Vata is the principle of kinetic energy in the body, and it operates through the nervous system, and controls bodily movement. Vata moves tissues and wastes. Kapha is the principle of potential energy, and controls bodily stability and lubrication. Pitta controls the body's balance of kinetic and potential energies. All of Pitta's processes are devoted to digestion of foods, ideas, thoughts and theories. Pitta rules the endocrinal and enzymatic systems.

The three principle Doshas are forces, not substances. Kapha is not mucus; it is the force which, within the body, causes mucus to arise. Pitta is not bile; it is the force that causes the production of bile. Vata is not gas but increased Vata causes increased gas. When the three principle Doshas are out of balance with each other, your body will also be unbalanced.

Kapha is the Water Dosha, but is also associated with Earth. For example, if you put soil into a water-filled jar and stir it well, it will stay suspended in the water. As soon as you stop stirring, it will settle on the bottom of the jar. Kapha reconciles liquids and solids when necessary, allowing balanced interaction between them. If the body is allowed to become too solid, illnesses like kidney stones and gallstones can occur. Likewise, if too much water is present and not enough solid earth, conditions like water retention can occur.

Pitta is associated with both Fire and Water. These two elements are usually antagonistic. Too much water will extinguish fire, whereas too much fire will evaporate water. However, fires *are* contained in water. Stomach acid is fire in water. If it is too concentrated or too great in volume, it will burn the stomach walls, sometimes causing ulcers. If the acid is too weak, food is unable to be digested. Pitta provides mediation to keep this uneasy alliance intact.

Vata is associated with Air and Ether. Air is mobile; its nature is to move and expand. Ether on the other hand is still and inert. Vata has the task of ensuring that there is just enough Ether/Space for Air to move in. Too much Ether/Space will lessen the effectiveness and vibrant movement of Air. In human beings this can lead to conditions such as emphysema and some bowel complaints that arise from the overuse of antibiotics. The Doshas therefore, offer opportunities for balance to sustain life comfortably. If they are out of balance for too long, ill-health occurs.

Qualities Of The Doshas
Vata is cold, light, irregular, quick moving, rarefied, and rough.
Pitta is hot, light, intense, fluid, and oily.
Kapha is cold, dense, stable, viscous, and smooth.

The Doshas are present in every cell, but tend to have affinities with certain organs and parts within our bodies, and therefore congregate in these areas:

Vata: bladder, bones, brain, colon, heart, lungs and nervous system.
Pitta: blood, brain, endocrinal system, eyes, liver, skin, small intestine and spleen.
Kapha: brain, lymphatic system, pericardial cavity, pleural cavity, joints, mouth and stomach.

Vata and Kapha have opposite qualities. Kapha permits energy to be stored and Vata causes stored energy to be released. Vata promotes change, but excessive change can lead to over-stimulation. Kapha promotes stasis, but excessive stasis can lead to inertia. Pitta is an arbitrator between the other two. Vata and Kapha congregate near one another for practical reasons. Within the heart, Vata provides the motion, and Kapha provides the lubrication. Too much motion uses up the lubricant; too much lubricant gums up the works.

Vata, Pitta, and Kapha are all essential to life, but can cause great harm if they are allowed to fall out of harmony with one another. Disharmony is not their fault; their job is difficult and very complex. Kapha must overcome the mutual indifference of Water and Earth and make them work together, Pitta must conquer the natural animosity which Water and Fire feel for one another; Vata is forced to use the inert Ether to try to control the capricious Air. The Doshas are very reactive and therefore the body cannot afford to store them. It must continuously eliminate them as they carry out their functions. Kapha is expelled via mucus, Pitta is regularly excreted through acid and bile, and Vata is eliminated both as gas and as muscular or nervous energy.

The Six Tastes

Regular motion and elimination of the Doshas is very important, as they continuously build up within our organism. Our body accumulates each Dosha out of the primary tastes that we consume. Tastes profoundly effect the balance of the Doshas within our system. Like the Doshas, they are derived from the five Great Elements. They are classified as follows:

Sweet   Composition: mainly Earth and Water. It increases Kapha, and decreases Pitta and Vata. It is cooling, heavy and unctuous. It nourishes and exhilarates the body and mind, and relieves hunger and thirst. It increases the efficiency of tissue growth and renewal.

Sour   Composition: mainly Earth and Fire. It increases Kapha and Pitta, and decreases Vata. It is heating, heavy, and unctuous. It refreshes the being, encourages elimination of wastes, lessens spasms and tremors, and improves appetite and digestion.

Salty   Composition: mainly Water and Fire. It increases Kapha and Pitta, and decreases Vata. It is heating, heavy, and unctuous. It eliminates wastes and cleanses the body, and increases the digestive capacity and appetite. It makes our muscles more relaxed.

Pungent   Composition: mainly Fire and Air. It is hot and spicy like chilli peppers. It increases Pitta and Vata, and decreases Kapha. It is heating, light, and dry. It flushes all types of secretions from the body, and reduces all Kapha-like tissues such as semen, milk and fat. It improves the appetite.

Bitter	Composition: mainly Air and Ether. It increases Vata, and decreases Pitta and Kapha. It is cooling, light, and dry. It purifies and dries all secretions and is also an anti-aphrodisiac. It tones and helps bring all tastes to normal balance. It increases appetite. It controls skin diseases and fevers.
Astringent	Composition: mainly of Air and Earth. It makes your mouth pucker. It increases Vata, and decreases Pitta and Kappa. It is cooling, light, and dry. It heals, purifies and constricts all parts of the body. It reduces all secretions. It is an anti-aphrodisiac.

Note: In the West we classify tastes into four categories: sweet, sour, salty and bitter. The *Ajur Vedic Sages* of the East say that, at the fundamental principle levels of all existence, there are six categories: the four already mentioned plus pungent and astringent.

Diet

Ideally, a balanced diet should contain meals that include all six tastes. Of course, you must consider keeping your relevant Dosha(s) balanced by being sparing on tastes that disturb balance, whilst including more of the foods that pacify your dominant Dosha, particularly during its seasonal time of year. The following guidance should help you in this task:

Vata	Requires sweet, sour and salty tastes and heavy, oily and hot qualities. Is unbalanced or irritated by pungent, bitter and astringent tastes and light, dry and cold qualities.
Pitta	Requires sweet, bitter and astringent tastes and heavy, dry and cold qualities. Is unbalanced or irritated by pungent, sour and salty tastes and light, oily and hot qualities.
Kapha	Requires pungent, bitter and astringent tastes and light dry and hot qualities. Is unbalanced or irritated by sweet, sour and salty tastes and heavy, oily and cold qualities.

Digestion

There is a popular saying that, "It is not what we eat, but what we digest that is most important". Even the healthiest foods can cause indigestion. It is important to remember that digestion begins in the mouth. The tongue samples the tastes and passes the information directly to the brain, which then classifies the protein, fat, and carbohydrate content. The necessary signals are then transmitted to glands within the digestive tract, so that they can secrete the correct mixture of digestive juices. By the time the food reaches the gut, all processes must be ready for it. Taste does not disappear from food even after it is digested. Each cell has its sense of taste and is effected by the taste of beneficial nutrients. The taste of food therefore influences consciousness. After digestion, tastes can alter within the body as follows:

Taste	Energy	After Digestion
Sweet	Cold	Sweet
Sour	Hot	Sour
Salty	Hot	Sweet
Pungent	Hot	Pungent
Bitter	Cold	Pungent
Astringent	Cold	Pungent

Sour, salty and pungent are always hot tastes, and sweet, bitter and astringent are always cold tastes.

People Types

From Vata, Pitta, and Kapha there are several permutations for constitutional types. These are:

Vata
Pitta
Kapha
Vata-Pitta
Pitta-Kapha
Vata-Kapha
Vata-Pitta-Kapha

One could also say that, in addition, you could add Pitta-Vata, Kapha-Pitta and Kapha-Vata depending on which Dosha is dominant.

Every individual is a mixture of all the Doshas, usually with one dominant followed closely by another. In order to assess your constitutional type, check through the following categories of information. If you feel that you belong partly in one constitution and partly in another, write down both. If in any one category you feel that you fit into all three constitutions, select the two which best characterise you. Whenever there is significant doubt or confusion, select Vata (the top Dosha).

While making your evaluation, keep in mind:

Vata is cold, dry and irregular.
Pitta is hot, oily and irritable.
Kapha is cold, wet and stable.

Most of us have a dual Dosha profile, and it will not always be easy to know which force predominates. If in doubt, ignore the difficult categories and pay more attention to the easier ones. Narrow shoulders and/or hips almost always occur in Vata people, broad shoulders and/or hips are characteristic of Kapha. People whose skins are dark or who tan easily have a lot of Vata, whilst those who burn easily, cannot tan at all, or tan very little, have a lot of Pitta.

Dosha Type Questionnaire
Read through the statements below and put the number that closest fits you alongside the statement. When you have finished, total up the numbers for each Dosha.

Number Classifications
0 - Never   4 - Often
1 - Rarely   5 - Mostly
2 - Occasionally   6 - Always
3 - Sometimes

Vata Types
• I am thin or slim —
• My body is narrow in the shoulders and/or hips —
• My joints often make cracking noises when I move them —
• I am a fidgety person —
• I don't sweat a lot —
• I enjoy being out in the sun —
• I suffer from the cold —
• I have poor peripheral circulation —
• My skin chaps easily —
• My skin is cool to touch —
• My appetite is irregular —
• I often suffer from indigestion —
• I suffer from chronic constipation —
• I love soupy, oily, hot foods —
• I suffer rapid fluctuations in energy levels —
• I have difficulty either falling asleep or staying asleep —
• I feel pain very easily —
• I detest routine —
• I am a changeable kind of person —

Total ____

Pitta Types
- I am an intense, hot and irritable type of person — —
- I am of medium height — —
- My skin is light in colour — —
- My skin reddens quickly in the sun, after exercise, or when blushing — —
- I have freckles and moles — —
- My hair is light in colour — —
- I sweat easily — —
- My appetite is mostly very good — —
- I love to eat — —
- I hate to miss a meal — —
- I move my bowels regularly and frequently — —
- I am a practical person — —
- I get angry easily — —
- I get impatient with people who are slower than me — —
- I sleep well — —
- If I overwork, I have difficulty sleeping — —
- I have strong opinions and stick to them — —
- I am dedicated to self-development — —
- I enjoy vigorous exercise — —
- I feel hungry and thirsty after a good workout — —

Total ——

Kapha Types
- I am heavyset — —
- I am a natural athlete — —
- I gain weight easily just by neglecting exercise and eating too much — —
- I have good general health most of the time — —
- I move my bowels about once every day — —
- I tolerate most kinds of weather — —
- I dislike humidity — —
- I am calm natured and slow to anger — —
- I have excellent stamina — —
- I can skip a meal without any real discomfort — —
- I have a tendency towards excess mucus, phlegm, sinus problems or asthma — —

- I am a slowish moving person —
- I have a soft skin with a palish complexion —
- The following words describe me:
  patient, calm, affectionate and forgiving —
- I am averse to too much change —
- I am apt to become greedy —
- I drop off to sleep easily —
- I am a sound sleeper —
- If I dream I normally have peaceful dreams —
- I prefer to avoid confrontation —

Total ———

You will be able to determine from this self-assessment whether you are a one-Dosha, a two-Dosha, or a multi-Dosha type of person. Most of us are a two-Dosha type, which means that two of the Doshas are more dominant, and one of them is predominant. When you have completed the questionnaire, the one with the most points is your predominant Dosha. If another Dosha has a score just a little less than that one, and the third Dosha is a long way behind, then you are a two-Dosha type. If your answers are fairly even throughout, you will be a very rare balanced Vata-Pitta-Kapha. To help you further identify your particular classification there follows a short summary of the dosha types:

Vata Types
Usually thin and have trouble gaining weight except when they excessively overeat, which they may do to help stabilise themselves, or to provide more energy for the next round of activity. Their bodies are usually narrow in the shoulders and hips and when moved, their joints often make a cracking noise. They also tend to be fidgety. Vata people are dry (they do not sweat as easily as other Dosha types), their skin usually chaps easily and they often get calluses and corns. Their hair tends to be thick, rough, dry and curly. Vata people do not like the cold and often have poor circulation in their fingers and toes. Their skin is usually cool to the touch, and they do not sweat a lot. Vata types are usually sun worshippers.

They have no interest in regular meals and can suffer from periods of constipation as a result of their inherent astringency. They love soupy, greasy, hot foods, but tend to go to extremes by either eating too many heavy stews or cheesy foods, or by completely abstaining from such eating.

Vata types are prone to up and down types of energy levels. They can have short bursts of highly energetic activity, followed by a period of complete exhaustion. They often try to sustain their energy by drinking copious amounts of coffee or other stimulants. Vata people often have difficulty with sleep. Either they have trouble falling asleep or staying asleep, or they avoid insomnia by maintaining such a high level of exhaustion that whenever they do permit themselves some rest, they sleep as if dead. They feel pain more than other types and detest loud noises. Their nervous systems seem to have less `insulation' than necessary and their innate drive to avoid pain may manifest itself as fear. They adore oil massage because it helps soothe and relax their overactive nervous system, and helps reduce sensitivity to pain, both physical and mental. These people live erratic lives because they find great difficulty in creating routine. If changeability characterises most of what you do, you are Vata-predominant.

Pitta Types

They tend to be intense, hot and irritable. They are usually of medium height, weight and strength. They are fair-skinned and burn quickly in the sun. They also blush a lot and get bright red after exercise. Their hair tends to be light in colour. Everyone whose hair is naturally red has quite a lot of Pitta in them.

These people sweat easily. Their appetites are usually good, and they love to eat. If they miss a meal they can get very irritable, and they love most foods and have excellent digestion. They have a tendency to loose stools and are rarely constipated.

Pittas have acute minds and tend to become quickly impatient around slower, less focused people. They usually sleep well because they feel it is sensible to do so. If, however, they become obsessed with work, they may have many sleepless nights. They apply the same intensity and competitiveness to everything they do, in work or play. The anger easily, even if they don't outwardly lose their tempers.

Kapha Types

Kapha types are capable of being natural athletes when exercising properly. Exercise is vital to this Dosha, otherwise their weight can become a problem. Most Kaphas are healthy people, especially if they do not overeat. They rarely feel the intense physical hunger that Vatas or Pittas do, since the sweet taste is innately strong in their constitutions. They only become attached to food as a means of emotional fulfilment.

Kapha people generally do not crave the same excitement and stimulation that Vata and Pitta people love, even from sex, although their appetites awaken once they are stimulated. Kapha people are stable, even somewhat slow, and tend to be complacent. Attachment to stable, enjoyable status quo makes these people averse to change and may lead them to become greedy, stubborn or reactionary. Kaphas need motivation and stimulation just as Vatas require balance and relaxation, and Pittas require a challenge. These people sleep soundly, often oversleeping.

One-Dosha types are really lucky in the sense that, once they know themselves, they always react confidently and effectively to specific stimuli. People with dual constitutions - Vata-Pitta, Pitta-Kapha and Vata-Kapha - have personalities which are always in a sense `split' under certain conditions; under one set of conditions, one Dosha will predominate, and under other conditions, the other Dosha comes to the fore. The inherent cohesion of personality which characterises purely Vata, Pitta, or Kapha people is less available to those of us who have dual characteristics, as we have to try to balance the demands of two very dissimilar principles. Most individuals are dual in constitution.

Vata-Pitta

These people generally have poor circulation and a love of heat which characterise Vatas, but their Pitta nature sets definite limits to their ability to endure heat. The Pitta in them makes them love to eat, but the Vata ensures they will have trouble digesting large meals. Many of their characteristics show a combination of Vata and Pitta. For example, they often have wavy hair caused by a combination of Vata's curliness and Pitta's straightness. (For example, my partner, Beverley, is a Vata-Pitta and she has straight hair on the surface with little waves underneath.)

Often the influences of Vata and Pitta alternate in the Vata-Pitta individual. When a Vata-Pitta is imbalanced, fear alternates with anger as a response to stress. This can lead to bullying and domination. The Pitta aspect feels the need to command, but the Vata aspect creates self-doubt about the person's capacity or fitness for command. The compromise involves the domination of beings weaker than oneself.

A healthy, balanced Vata-Pitta needs Vata's capacity for original thought and Pitta's expertise at application of theory. Vata and Pitta have lightness and intensity as their common qualities. Proper direction of this intensity calls for harnessing the lightness for intensive self-development. Otherwise the Vata tendency toward addiction for pain control and the Pitta predilection for addiction to amplified intensity, will drag the Vata-Pitta individual into deeper states of addiction than either Vata or Pitta people can separately know. Vata-Pitta types mostly need stability. They need to be weighed down with the heaviness that characterises Kapha, which is the least influential factor in their personality equation. The sweet taste is most important for them.

Pitta-Kapha

These people probably adjust better than any other constitution to the confusion, irregularity and constant change that characterises today's world, because they combine Kapha's stability and Pitta's adaptability. Many of the people who achieve all-round success in life are usually Pitta-Kaphas. Pitta's active metabolism balances Kapha's powerful physique to promote good physical health, and

Pitta's anger is well-tempered by Kapha's cautiousness to encourage good mental balance. Though Pitta-Kaphas usually prefer temperate climates, they can easily endure extremes of heat or cold. They enjoy and profit by vigorous exercise, including sex.

Pitta-Kaphas are often over-confident, smug and filled with self-satisfaction, and this sometimes leads to an unrealistic view of events around them. They enjoy flattery and disregard criticism. They often make excellent athletes, combining Pitta's energy and Kapha's endurance. This type does not like missing meals. Pitta-Kapha's health is usually excellent.

Vata-Kapha
These people are less bulky than other Kapha Dosha types. They are usually tall but of average build and well-proportioned, rather like Pitta types. They do not suffer from physical coldness as much as Vata types, but have an emotional need for heat. They detest cold weather. They often suffer from constipation, digestive problems, respiratory disorders, and have lots of mucus. Vata-Kaphas often overdo things and are not very discrete. They can swing from being deeply secretive to light and open. They often misjudge situations and people. They take rebuke very seriously and can be deeply hurt. Vata-Kaphas mostly project a sense of inner stability, tending to be even-tempered unless overstressed when they can seem alarmed. They can be quick and efficient in action, yet they are prone to hoard and store.

Three Dosha Types
These are rare. If the Doshas are perfectly balanced, they stand a chance of living a long and healthy life. However, should imbalances occur, the disadvantage is trying to balance three Doshas, as opposed to two, in order to return to a balanced state.

Three Reversed Sub-Dosha Types
In addition to the Dosha types so far mentioned, I have found that there are people who fall into what I call the reversed Sub-Dosha types. They have Pitta predominating over Vata, Kapha over Pitta, and Kapha over Vata.

Pitta-Vata
They are muscular and solid, and of medium build. They tend to have high energy levels and move quite fast. They are assertive and often deep thinkers. No challenge is too great for these types, and they have great self-confidence. However, they can feel somewhat insecure when confronted by fear.

Kapha-Pitta
The solid structure of Kapha is even more evident in this type. Kapha-Pittas usually have strong muscular bodies, but can be lazy and succumb to gaining weight. They tend to be oval or round shaped people and are slow moving and more relaxed than Pitta-Kaphas. They have very good stamina and need lots of regular exercise, but sometimes they need to be motivated.

Kapha-Vata
These people are more solidly built and move more slowly than Vata-Kaphas as they tend to be very relaxed people. They make great athletes as they have vast amounts of stamina. Like Vata-Kaphas, they can suffer from digestive problems and need to wrap up in cold weather.

The idea of constitutional types helps to explain how Mother Nature has given each of us a personal blend of tendencies. You cannot alter your constitution, but self-awareness of your type can enhance and optimise every part of your life.

Vata, Pitta And Kapha Tastes
These Dosha tastes are found in all of nature. They are within seasons, foods, spices, vitamins, minerals, herbs, places, temperatures, types of weather and occupations - in fact, everything around and within us.

Balancing The Doshas
In order to maintain our personal equilibrium, we need to concentrate on four broad areas of our everyday lives: diet, daily routine, seasonal routine, and exercise.

Whether you are a Vata type or not, Vata is the `king' Dosha. When Vata is balanced, it can help bring the other two Doshas into line. Vata is very sensitive and changeable. They like variety, but if changes occur too often or quickly, then exhaustion occurs. Those with a predominance of Vata need to have plenty of sleep and rest, preferably in well-ventilated places. They require frequent fluid intake, frequent meals, warmth, peace and quiet, and regular habits.

Eating For Balance
Vata Foods
Sweet, sour and salty foods are good for Vata people. They keep the system working smoothly. Bitter, pungent and astringent foods tend to dry the system and in Vata people can cause feelings of anxiety, insecurity and some distress.

Grains - Wheat is good for Vatas, but should be taken in moderate quantities. Well-cooked oats and rice are good. Buckwheat, corn, millet and rye all tend to be drying and therefore are not as good for Vata types. All grain products must be cooked with plenty of water and with butter, ghee or oil added to reduce the dryness. Rice gruel is very good if your digestion is out of sorts. Bread made from yeast is not very good for Vatas, because of the gases it produces during digestion.

Vegetables - Vata types best assimilate rough vegetables that are well cooked. The best vegetables for them to eat are asparagus, beets, carrots, celery, green beans, okra, cooked onions, parsnips, radishes, rutabagas, turnips, sweet potatoes and water chestnuts. Raw salads of leafy greens like parsley, coriander leaf, lettuce, spinach and Brussels sprouts are all acceptable for Vatas, providing they are eaten with oily or creamy dressings. Cucumbers and squashes can be consumed occasionally if they are well cooked with oil. Tomatoes are best taken infrequently and in minute amounts. However, tomato sauce with pasta meals is acceptable.

Vatas must reduce or avoid aubergine and peppers. Potatoes must be eaten in moderation. Mushrooms can occasionally be taken in moderation, but only when well-boiled, steamed or well-cooked and then served with an oily dressing.

Fruits - Most fruits are good for Vatas, except those that are naturally astringent like cranberries and pomegranates, or those that are drying like apples. However, cranberry sauce and pomegranate syrup is acceptable, as are stewed or baked apples or apple sauce. All dried fruits, even figs and grapes, are inappropriate for Vatas unless they are reconstituted to normal juiciness by soaking in water.

Vatas must avoid all unripe fruit, especially bananas which are astringent when unripe. Very ripe bananas are soothing to the digestive juices and are therefore acceptable.

The best fruits for Vatas include apricots, avocados, bananas, berries, cherries, coconut, dates, figs, grapefruit, grapes, lemons, mangoes, melons, nectarines, oranges, papaya, peaches, pears, persimmons, pineapples and plums.

Flesh Foods - All meats must only be taken in small amounts because Vatas have a very sensitive digestion. In most cases, dairy products can fulfil their protein requirements. However, if flesh foods are required, the best are chicken, turkey, fresh fish and venison. Red meats are best avoided but, if taken, a little well cooked lamb or goat is acceptable.

Dairy Produce - Low fat cream, milk and soft cheeses provide a good amount of protein. Low fat yogurt blended with water and spiced with ginger or cumin helps to reduce Vata within the system. Hard cheeses must be only taken in small amounts and not too often. Likewise, eggs should be used sparingly, usually no more than two per week.

Legumes - These are high in protein that is difficult to digest, and during digestion they give off nitrogenous waste. Nitrogen is a gas that increases Vata and adds toxins to the blood. Avoid all legumes except chickpeas, mung beans, pink lentils and very small amounts of tofu. During cooking, use turmeric to prevent toxins entering the blood, cumin and coriander seeds to enkindle the digestion, and ginger, garlic or asafoetida to prevent Vata disturbances. Another tip to prevent Vata imbalances is to add a little oil to the cooking pot.

Nuts and Seeds - Almonds are the best nut to eat but they must be soaked for at least eight hours before eating. A few almonds eaten each morning will be of great nutritional benefit. Pumpkinseed is a brain tonic and sesame seeds are also very good taken in moderation. All nuts and seeds are good for Vata people in small quantities and preferably in butters or milks.

Oils - Sesame is the best oil for Vatas. Safflower oil is of the least benefit, but all oils in moderation are good for Vatas.

Sweeteners - Sweets help reduce excess Vata, therefore they can use any sweetener in moderation, except white sugar which is toxic for them. Uncooked honey can be used freely, but excessive use of sugars can eventually increase Vata.

Spices - All spices are good for Vatas and Vata-Kaphas in small quantities. Garlic and ginger are the best, but never be tempted to overuse spices, because excess of anything will eventually increase Vata and throw it out of balance.

CAUTION: Due to Vata's addictive nature, stimulants must be kept to an absolute minimum, especially caffeine and sugar. Vatas can benefit from an occasional small glass of wine diluted with water, with or after a meal. Larger quantities of alcohol can be deadly, and Vatas should avoid all alcoholic drinks that are known to have chemical additives. Beer is not as beneficial as wine because of its yeast content.

Pitta Foods
Sweet, bitter and astringent-cold tastes are best for Pitta people, and sour, salty and pungent-hot tastes should be avoided. Pittas should especially avoid too much meat, alcohol, salt and too many eggs. All these substances arouse Pitta's natural aggressiveness and compulsiveness. Grains, fruit and vegetables have a cooling effect on the Pitta heat and should form the majority of the Pitta diet. A vegetarian diet is favourable for Pittas.

Grains - Barley is the supreme grain for Pittas because it is cooling and drying, and helps reduce excess stomach acid. Rice, oats and wheat are also beneficial. Buckwheat, corn, millet and rye are all heating and should be consumed infrequently and in minute quantities, if at all. Yeasted bread is not very good for Pittas but yeast free varieties are acceptable.

Vegetables - Pittas can eat as many vegetables as they wish, but avoiding radishes and tomatoes. The use of garlic should be kept to an absolute minimum. Beets, carrots and daiken are purifying to the liver and help control Pitta, if it is not out of balance. However, if Pitta is disturbed, they should be avoided. Steamed onions lose their pungency and are therefore acceptable for Pitta. Avoid vegetables when they are sour or pungent.

The best vegetables for Pittas to eat are asparagus, broccoli, Brussels sprouts, cabbage, cucumber, cauliflower, celery, cress, green beans, leafy greens, lettuce, mushrooms, okra, peas, parsley, potatoes, sprouts, squashes and water chestnuts.

Fruits - Pittas should eat sweet fruits and avoid sour fruits completely, especially including cherries, grapes, oranges, pineapples and pomegranates. Any berries, if ripe and sweet, are acceptable. Papaya is too hot and bananas, even when ripe and sweet, have a sour after digestive effect and are not acceptable for Pittas.

The following fruits, when ripe, are best for Pittas apples, apricots, avocados, coconut, dried fruits, figs, mangoes, melons, nectarines, peaches, pears, persimmons and plums.

Flesh Foods - Pitta people should eat seafood sparingly because it is hot and tends to cause allergies. Egg yolks are hot and whites are cooling. Pittas can digest flesh foods, but should take them in very small amounts, if at all, because they encourage aggression and irritability. Chicken, turkey, rabbit and venison are permissible for Pitta people.

Dairy Produce - All sweet dairy products like milk, unsalted butter and ghee are good for Pitta types. However, Pittas must avoid sour dairy produce. Low fat yogurt can be consumed if it is spiced with cinnamon or coriander plus a few drops of lemon juice.

Legumes - Pitta people have little difficulty digesting most foods, but should be wary of legumes because the same toxins that effect Vatas also aggravate Pittas. Red and yellow lentils are acceptable in small amounts, but the best are black lentils, chickpeas, mung beans and tofu.

Nuts and seeds - Most nuts and seeds are too hot and oily for Pitta types. Coconut is good for Pitta people because even though it is oily, it is also very cooling, and fresh coconut milk is excellent for aggravated Pitta. Sunflower seeds and pumpkinseed are also permitted.

Oils - Pittas should avoid most oils, but may consume small amounts of almond oil, or larger amounts of coconut, olive or sunflower oils.

Sweeteners - Pitta is relieved by sweets. Of all people, Pittas can best enjoy sweet foods, including sugar, because sweets reduce heat. Molasses is hot and Pittas should not use it. Long-term overuse of honey, which is also hot, could aggravate Pitta.

Spices - Spices increase Pitta's aggressive and impatient nature. Pittas should only use the cooling spices. Mustard and salt should be eliminated or drastically reduced from dietary intake.

The best spices for Pittas are: cardamom, cinnamon, coriander, fennel and turmeric. Tiny amounts of cumin and black pepper are permitted.

CAUTION: Alcohol and tobacco are too hot for Pittas. An occasional beer may, however, help a Pitta to relax. Tea is astringent and may be used occasionally. Coffee is pungent and is irritating to the liver and should not be used habitually.

Kapha Foods

Bitter, pungent and astringent tastes are the ones for Kaphas. They invigorate their bodies and minds. They should avoid sweet, sour and salty substances, which keep them set in their ways. Kaphas should never eat greasy or fried food, and should keep dairy products to an absolute minimum. Fats are the worst food for Kapha constitutions whereas vegetables are the best, but even these should be taken in limited amounts.

Grains - Kapha people require fewer grain products than Vata or Pitta people do. The hot, drying grains buckwheat and millet are best for Kaphas, followed by barley, rice and corn. Grains are best roasted. All bread should be either toasted or avoided. Wheat is too heavy for Kaphas.

Vegetables - All vegetables except potatoes, tomatoes and water chestnuts are acceptable for Kaphas. However over-sweet, over-sour or very juicy vegetables should not be eaten. Kaphas can enjoy most vegetables as often as they wish and in large quantities. Surface-grown vegetables must take preference over root varieties. Kaphas can eat vegetables raw, steamed or stir-fried. Kapha types thrive on peppers and usually love chillies, cayenne and other hot, pungent spices, sometimes to their discomfort. If Pitta gets aggravated through this misuse it can quickly be brought back into balance by taking a small amount of ghee.

Fruits - Kapha people should avoid very sweet and very sour fruits, and any fruits which are very juicy. Dried fruits like prunes are good but the best fruits for Kaphas are apples, apricots, cranberries, mangoes, peaches, pears and pomegranates.

Flesh Foods - Kapha people rarely need any flesh foods because their flesh is adequately nourished by other foods. When they do eat flesh it should be roasted, broiled, baked or cooked in some other dry way. They must avoid fried foods. The best meats for Kaphas to eat are chicken, rabbit and venison. Seafood and eggs are also acceptable.

Dairy Produce - Kaphas have little need for most dairy produce. Small amounts of ghee and goat's milk are acceptable.

Legumes - Kaphas should not overeat legumes because their bodies do not require large amounts of proteins. Legumes are, however, much better for Kaphas than meat. They should avoid the heaviest legumes such as black lentils, kidney beans and soya beans. Well cooked tofu is good for Kaphas only in small amounts, as large quantities are apt to increase Kapha.

The best legumes for Kaphas are black beans, mung beans, pinto beans and red lentils.

Nuts and Seeds - Most nuts and seeds are too oily for Kapha people. Pumpkinseed and sunflower seeds can be eaten occasionally.

Oils - Kapha people should avoid the use of oils. If, for any reason, they use oil, it should be one of the following: almond, corn, safflower or sunflower oil.

Sweeteners - Kapha is increased by sweets, and Kapha people should not use any sweeteners except raw honey which helps reduce Kapha.

Spices - Kaphas find spices useful to awaken their organisms, and they can use all spices except salt which increases Kapha directly. Kaphas, like Vatas, benefit from the use of ginger and garlic.

CAUTION: Only the pure Kapha Dosha people can really benefit from the occasional use of stimulants. Tea is good for them, and coffee is acceptable. Kaphas should avoid beer, and drink only wine or diluted spirits.

Dual Dosha Constitutional Types

Vatta-Pitta and Pitta-Vatta people should generally follow a Vata-controlling diet in autumn and winter, and a Pitta-controlling diet in spring and summer. Pungent tastes increase both Vata and Pitta, and sweet tastes control both these Doshas. Therefore Vata-Pitta and Pitta-Vata people should be careful to avoid spicy, pungent food because of the anger these create, and search for sweetness in everything they do, especially eating.

Pitta-Kapha and Kapha-Pitta should follow a Pitta controlling diet from late spring through to early autumn, and a Kapha-controlling diet from late autumn through to early spring. Bitter and astringent tastes are best for Pitta-Kaphas and Kapha-Pittas.

Vata-Kapha and Kapha-Vata should follow a Vata controlling diet in summer and autumn and a Kapha controlling diet in winter and spring. Since both Vata and Kapha are cold and need heat, Vata-Kapha and Kapha-Vata people should prefer sour, salty and pungent (the *hot* tastes) to sweet, bitter and astringent (the *cold* tastes). In summer and autumn sour and salty tastes may be preferred but should be balanced with sweet. In winter and spring, pungent tastes may be preferred but should be balanced with bitter and astringent tastes.

From this information and the questionnaire you are now able to assess your body type and choose the foods to balance your dominant Dosha. Even then, if you don't enjoy a particular food or if it gives you any discomfort during digestion, it's probably one that you should exclude from your diet. Before embarking on a Dosha diet personal programme, it might be advantageous to rest your digestion and have a small clean-out of your system. This is accomplished quite simply as follows:

Purification Routine

Before embarking on this five day clean-out, it is important to ensure that your bowels are working effectively. If not, I advise a visit to your GP who will probably prescribe a mild laxative. Take this until you have proper bowel movements, then commence the following routine:

First Day

Eat a small breakfast and midday meal, and a light evening meal. Have a warm drink about two hours before going to bed and make sure that you have an early night.

Second Day

Again have a small breakfast and midday meal, and a light evening meal. In between meals, increase your daily intake of fresh, filtered water. Drink several glasses between meals. If it is too bland, add a very small amount of non-acidic juice. Have a warm drink about two hours before going to bed. Again have an early night.

Third Day

Have a nice, restful day drinking only liquids. At meal times you may have a glass of warm, non-acidic fruit juice, such as pear juice or very diluted apple juice. Have one glassful at each mealtime and if you require more fluids between these times, drink only clean, warm or cold water to suite your personal taste.

Take things easy during the day; maybe go for a very short walk in the morning and afternoon. Avoid arduous or physical tasks. Just watch TV, read or listen to music. If you feel faint or uncomfortable, take a tablespoonful of honey or raw cane sugar in warm water and lie down for a few minutes.

Fourth Day

Eat a light breakfast of hot cereal or creamed rice/home-made rice pudding with a little butter or milk and a small quantity of sugar. If you still feel hungry follow this with a glass of diluted juice.

Do not eat again until midday, then have a nice meal (don't overfill your stomach). Avoid spices or salty foods. Do not eat again until early evening, then have a nice meal made from the foods suitable for your constitutional type.

Fifth Day
Eat a light breakfast made from foods on your list. Eat a substantial midday meal, but don't overfill your stomach. Eat your next meal in the early evening, and ensure that it is finished, if possible, at least three hours before bedtime. When you are eating your meals, chew your food thoroughly before swallowing, eat slowly and relax. Try to carry these good habits forward into each day of your life. From now on, eat a light breakfast, your main meal about midday and a light nourishing evening meal at least three hours before bedtime. When planning meals, be aware of your Dosha type and the time of year.

General Information
Each of us has our own Dosha constitution and the tastes within it are reflected in everything we do and in everything around us. There are special risk times for the appropriate Dosha type:

Vata predominates - after eating and before digestion begins, during pre-dawn and late afternoon hours, and in old age. It is accumulated during cold, dry, windy weather. Its season is mid-autumn to mid-spring.

Pitta predominates - during digestion, at midday and midnight, and in middle age. It is accumulated during hot weather, particularly when humidity builds up. Its season is mid-summer to the first part of autumn.

Kapha predominates - after digestion during assimilation, in the daytime, at dawn and dusk. It is accumulated during cold, damp, rainy, sleety weather. Its season is mid-spring to mid-summer.
To benefit from the information provided in this chapter:

- Read through the chapter again.
- Answer the questionnaire.
- Determine your Dosha type.
- Check your Dosha season.
- Now apply the tips and information given throughout the chapter for your type.
- Ensure that you adhere to the advice for your type, especially during your season.

Summary

- The universe is formed from three primary qualities: Sattva - Balance; Rajas - Motion; and Tamas - Form.
- From these primary qualities came Five Great Elements: Earth, Water, Fire, Air, and Ether.
- The Five Great Elements condense to three principles of matter: Vatta, Pitta and Kapha.
- Within each individual human constitution these three Principle Force-Doshas are blended, usually with one of them being dominant.
- Vata operates within Space and Air and is the principle of kinetic energy in our bodies.
- Pitta works with Fire and Water and is the principle of digestion, and governs the endocrinal and enzymatic systems.
- Kapha works with Earth and Water. It is the principle of potential energy, and controls stability and lubrication.
- There are six primary tastes within nature: sweet, sour, salty, bitter, pungent and astringent.
- Your body accumulates each Dosha out of the primary tastes that you consume.
- Tastes profoundly effect the balance of the Doshas within your system.
- Incorrect ingestion or use of primary tastes can cause imbalances within you.
- Doshas are not only affected by foods but also by health, well-being, illness, temperatures, times of day, seasons, kinds of weather, and many other factors.
- It is therefore imperative that your Doshas are in correct proportion to your constitutional type.
- A good knowledge of your constitutional type and careful programme of exercise, diet, etc. can lead to a healthier, more satisfying, longer life.

Chapter Six

Building Blocks Of The Body

True harmony is pure balance, which very soon begets;
A beauteous rhythm of energy, between poles and opposites.

Healthy eating means choosing foods that give us the essential nutrients required by our body to grow, repair itself and carry out vital chemical processes. In the last chapter we discussed the types of food suitable for our individual constitutional character. Now we will discover what elements are contained within our food and how they work together to keep us alive and healthy.

Each person's needs differ depending on constitutional type, age, way of life, metabolic rate and genetic make-up. Carbohydrates, proteins and fats are all needed to provide energy and for building and repairing body tissues. A daily intake of fibre is also very important to assist with correct digestion. Fibre helps to keep the colon healthy and form stools for correct evacuation of waste. Vitamins and minerals are essential to help the body function correctly. A regular intake of vitamins and minerals is essential, but only small doses are required.

In modern times, most foods have additives in the form of colorants, preservatives, taste enhancers and tenderisers. Unfortunately, these additives are mostly toxic and neutralise many of the vital vitamins and minerals that are naturally in the foods. I would advise that, where possible, you buy foods that are organically grown and, in the case of dairy products, that are free-range.

Carbohydrates

Carbohydrates are highly nutritious and, when eaten, release energy very quickly. Large quantities are essential for people who do hard, physical work. The body breaks them down into glucose which is ready for immediate use, and reserves are stored as glycogen in the muscles and liver. If excess amounts are taken in and not burnt up, they are converted and stored as fat.

Carbohydrate molecules contain carbon, hydrogen and oxygen atoms, and include starches and sugars, but refined cane sugar and sugarbeet are now the major sources of carbohydrates for human consumption. They consist of sugar (sucrose) and are the sweetest of the natural carbohydrates in our diet. Refined sugar is not as filling as other carbohydrate foods. We should ensure that starches make up most of our daily carbohydrate intake. The best sources are bread, oats, rice and other grains, beans, peas and potatoes. We all make the assumption that white bread is bad because we hear so much about how wholemeal bread is good for us. In fact white bread is also good for us, it is just that wholemeal bread is even better.

To improve our diet, we should be eating more bread and potatoes and less red meat, fat and refined sugar. Occasional small helpings of cakes, biscuits and puddings made with white sugar and flour do no harm but should not form a regular part of our diet because of their high fat content. If you feel the need to snack, replace these with vegetables such as carrots or a low-fat sandwich.

Proteins

Proteins form the basic structure of bones, tendons, muscles and most tissues. They are the building blocks for repair, regeneration and new cell growth. They are also vital in their role in hormones and enzymes, for regulating and controlling the body's chemistry and functions. A protein molecule contains carbon, hydrogen, oxygen and nitrogen atoms, and can also occasionally contain phosphorous and sulphur atoms. A body-building protein molecule contains carbon, hydrogen, oxygen and nitrogen atoms, and sometimes phosphorous and sulphur. It contains a chain (or chains) of amino acids which are built up in the body from elements extracted from digested foods. Any excess of protein is converted into glucose to provide energy or is stored as fat.

Proteins can deliver the same energy pro-rata as carbohydrates, but their prime use is as building and repair materials. Therefore, proteins are needed in much smaller quantities than carbohydrates. Many people incorrectly think that red meat is the best provider of proteins, whereas in reality most people in the West have their intake of protein from a variety of foods such as fish, eggs, cheese, yogurt, milk, bread, beans, peas, breakfast cereals, nuts and even potatoes.

The amino acids in proteins have to be in certain combinations so that the body can use them. Many animal foods such as meat and dairy products have the right mixture, but many also contain too much fat. Plant protein is much better: oats, wheat, and pulses contain protein and starch with little fat, but need to be combined to provide the right mix of amino acids. Vegetable protein with small amounts of animal protein is a good combination, such as: fish and rice, bread and cheese sandwiches, and beans on toast. In the case of vegetarians, those who eat a wide range of foods will get plenty of proteins without worrying about combinations in the diet as sources of protein.

Fats

A healthy diet must contain some fats as they form vital parts of the structure of our body cells. Fats also lie under our skin as insulation and to cushion our organs. They are necessary for the absorption into the body of vitamins A, D, E and K; they also make food tastier and easier to swallow. Fats are composed of fatty acids containing hydrogen and oxygen attached to chains of carbon atoms. Edible fats have an even number of carbons in the chain.

Fatty acids in which all possible chemical bonds are used are known as saturated fats. Monounsaturated fatty acids have one unused bonding site for a hydrogen atom in the molecule, whilst polyunsaturated fats have several. Animal fats are mainly saturated and generally solid at room temperature. Vegetable fats are mostly unsaturated, are generally liquid at room temperature and are usually known as oils.

A high intake of saturated fatty acids seems to make the body form too much cholesterol. Some cholesterol is needed for a healthy brain and nervous system and for the production of hormones. However, excess cholesterol can cause gallstones and coat the inside of the arteries, eventually impeding blood circulation. To avoid this danger, we should eat less fat and try to make sure that the little we do eat is mainly unsaturated. In a diet where fat consumption is low, the occasional cake, fried food or slice of buttered toast presents no danger.

Foods to take in very tiny amounts include meat and dairy products such as cream, hard cheeses, eggs, hard margarine, and some soft margarine, as well as peanuts and peanut butter and products containing palm or coconut oil. These are all high in saturated fat. Olive oil and fish oils are monounsaturates.

Sources of polyunsaturates are oily fish such as herring, mackerel, trout and salmon, also oils from sunflower seed, maize-corn, walnuts, safflower seed, sesame seed and grapeseed. Eating oily fish, peas and beans is now thought to help in clearing cholesterol deposits already formed in the arteries. The best oils are those labelled `cold-pressed', `virgin' or `extra virgin'. Other oils will have been treated with heat or chemicals which can convert unsaturated to saturates. Never eat oils that are rancid.

Fibre
Fibre adds bulk and has little or no nutritional value. It is found in large quantities in bread, rice and bran, and in all cereals. It is also found in leafy and root vegetables, fruits, salads, beans, peas and other pulses. The body is unable to digest or absorb fibre, and its greatest value is as a purgative. It pushes food through the system more quickly so hastening the excretion of waste and harmful substances. It keeps the digestive tract healthy and carries the waste away, preventing constipation and reducing the risk of bowel cancer. Fibre gives us a feeling of fullness and satisfaction from our meals and this then helps prevent us from overeating. Many foods now have fibre added to them. However, if you eat plenty of whole foods in your daily meals, you will usually take in a sufficient amount of fibre to satisfy the daily requirement.

Tips On Eating

- Eat breakfast each day, however small, and perhaps two other meals.
- Never eat a large meal too late in the day.
- Avoid eating foods that make you feel uncomfortable, acidy or bloated.
- Eat your food when it is as fresh as possible, and avoid stale or old food.
- Always relax before having your meal.
- Never eat food that is too hot.
- Chew your food carefully and eat slowly.

Vitamins And Minerals

Vitamins and minerals are vital to the efficient functioning of the body but are only needed in small amounts. They play a critical part in the bodily processes and provide protection against infections and diseases. The best natural sources of vitamins and minerals are found in fresh, fresh-frozen, unprocessed fruit and vegetables, dairy products, cereal foods, meat, eggs and fish. Most of these nutrients dissolve in water or are destroyed by too much heat. It is, therefore, important to only lightly cook or eat fresh raw fruit and salads when possible. Some vegetables can also be eaten raw. Salads containing chopped spinach, carrots, mushrooms, cabbage, lettuce, shelled peas, runner beans, cauliflower, radish, celery and tomatoes provide vitamins and minerals in natural abundance.

To ensure that you retain all the essential nutrients in the vegetables, the best way to cook them is to steam or stir-fry so causing the least loss of nutrients. If boiling vegetables or fruit, add them to boiling water and cook for the shortest possible time. Add the cooking water to soups or stews, as it can contain a rich supply of nutrients. If you use salt, be very sparing in the amounts you add to food as salt causes the body to retain waste products and water. Those suffering from high blood pressure must avoid salt.

Oxidisation And Antioxidants

Rust is the result of oxidation, a chemical reaction between iron and oxygen (usually from the air). This happens not only in our outside environment but also within our bodies. Damage is caused to cells by oxidising chemicals active in the body known as `free radicals'. Currently, free radicals are suspected of contributing to or being partly responsible for ageing, genetic damage, lung disease, nerve damage, degenerative diseases, immunity weakness, inflammatory diseases including arthritis, atherosclerosis, etc..

Many vitamins and minerals have antioxidant properties which can drastically reduce the presence of free radicals in the blood.

Vitamins

Research has proven that food contains minute quantities of substances required for normal growth and the maintenance of health. These substances are now known as vitamins - essential food accessories. The reason vitamins are so important is that they need to be present to make enzymes work.

Enzymes

These catalysts facilitate the correct extraction and alchemy of chemicals from food. They also play a vital role in the body's metabolism. If enzymes were not present or not working effectively, all bodily functions would soon cease to work properly, and disease and death would quickly ensue.

Main Vitamins

Vitamin A	(Retinol)	Fat-soluable
Found in:	yellow/orange vegetables, green vegetables, tomatoes.	

Preformed Vitamin A		
Found in:	full-fat dairy produce, liver, kidneys, eggs, fish/liver oils, apricots, peaches.
Benefits:	night vision; healthy skin and mucous membranes; resistance to infection. Sometimes used to treat acne.
Warning:	large doses can be toxic.
Effects of Deficiency:	night blindness; ear, eye and respiratory infections; dry skin; dull hair and hair loss; weight loss; stunted growth.

Vitamin B1	(Thiamin, Aneurin)	Water-soluble
Found in:	wheat germ and wholegrain cereals, brown rice, fortified white flour and products, brewer's yeast, seafood, liver, meat, poultry, pulses, nuts, potatoes, milk.
Benefits:	converts blood sugars into energy; healthy muscles and nervous system; countering pains; helps maintain healthy heart rhythm.
Effects of Deficiency:	loss of appetite, constipation; fatigue; depression, irritability; lack of concentration; shortness of breath; slow heart.
Severe:	beriberi and eventual death.

Vitamin B2	(Riboflavin)	Water-soluble
Found in:	liver, kidney, meat, poultry, eggs, cheese, yogurt, wholegrain cereals, fortified cereals, brewer's yeast/yeast extract, fish, green vegetables, pulses.
Benefits:	metabolism of carbohydrates, fats and proteins; healthy skin and mucous membranes.
Effects of Deficiency:	inflammation of tongue and lips, sores; scaly scalp and hair loss; sensitivity to light; trembling; dizziness; insomnia.

Vitamin B3	(Niacin)	Water-soluble
Found in:	some cereals including rice (not maize), fortified white flour and products, meat, liver, poultry, kidney, yeast extract/brewer's yeast, eggs, fish, nuts (especially peanuts) cheese, peas and beans, globe artichokes, dried fruit.	
Benefits:	efficient blood circulation; control of blood cholesterol; healthy adrenal glands; healthy skin and nervous system; healthy appetite.	
Effects of Deficiency:	loss of appetite, nausea, gastrointestinal ulcers, diarrhoea; dermatitis; fatigue, headaches; insomnia, irritability, depression; inflamed tongue.	
Severe:	pellagra (dementia with dermatitis and diarrhoea)	

Vitamin B5	(Pantothenic acid)	Water-soluble
Found in:	all living matter and most foods, but especially beans, egg yolk, legumes, liver, oranges, peanuts, wheat germ, wholegrain cereals. Also manufactured in the intestine.	
Benefits:	metabolism of fats and carbohydrates; healthy skin and hair; healthy nervous system; production of antibodies against infection.	
Effects of Deficiency:	deficiency is very rare in humans. rare symptoms may include increased susceptibility to allergy and infections; asthma; cramp; fatigue; insomnia.	

Vitamin B6	(Pyridoxine)	Water-soluble
Found in:	most foods, but especially green vegetables, brewer's yeast/yeast extracts, fish, pulses, prunes, raisins, soya beans, flour, nuts, wholegrain cereals, milk.	
Benefits:	production of antibodies; red blood cell formation; metabolism of protein.	
Effects of Deficiency:	deficiency not reported in humans.	

Vitamin B12	(Cyanocobalamin)	Water-soluble
Found in:	egg yolk, liver, kidney, wheat germ, nuts, oats, brewer's yeast/yeast extract.	
Benefits:	proper functioning of folic acid; red blood cell formation; healthy nervous system; synthesis of nucleic acids and proteins; metabolism of fats, proteins and carbohydrates; prevention of cell degeneration.	
Effects of Deficiency:	loss of appetite; fatigue; irritability; anaemia.	
Severe:	degeneration of nervous system, leading to moving and speech difficulties.	
Vitamin C	(Ascorbic acid)	Water-soluble
Found in:	fruits and fruit juices, citrus fruits and blackcurrants, rose hips and syrup, potatoes, chillies and peppers.	
Benefits:	healthy skin, bone, tendons, cartilage, ligaments, blood vessels, gums, teeth; energy production and growth; resistance to infection; wound healing; iron absorption; control of blood cholesterol.	
Effects of Deficiency:	bleeding and/or soft gums, loose teeth; low resistance to infections; tender joints; muscle degeneration; fatigue; weakness; irritability; anaemia.	
Severe:	scurvy, which can be fatal.	
Vitamin D	(Cholecalciferol) Produced by action of sunlight on human skin	Fat-soluble
Found in:	liver, fish-liver oils, kippers, mackerel, sardines, tuna, tinned salmon, margarine, egg yolk, evaporated milk, full-fat dairy products, malted milk drinks, sprouted seeds.	
Benefits:	absorption of calcium and phosphorus for healthy bones and teeth.	
Warning:	large doses can be toxic.	
Effects of Deficiency:	bone deformities, dental caries; cramp, muscle weakness.	
Severe:	rickets and osteomalacia (equivalent of rickets in adults).	

Vitamin E	(Tocopherol)	Fat-soluble
Found in:	most foods but especially vegetable oils, egg yolks, wholegrain cereals, wheat germ, green vegetables, nuts and seeds, pulses, margarine.	
Benefits:	healthy cell membranes; may retard effects of aging; healthy blood cells; blood clotting; resistance to infection; possibly aids fertility.	
Effects of Deficiency:	(rare) dull hair; muscle weakness; possible enlarged prostate gland; miscarriage.	

Vitamin K	(Menadione) Water-soluble Synthesised by bacteria in large intestine.	
Found in:	green vegetables, especially brassicas, seaweed (kelp), liver, potatoes, eggs, wheat germ.	
Effects of Deficiency:	Very rare, but may be caused by long-term use of antibiotics: bleeding beneath the skin; nose bleed; diarrhoea.	

Biotin	(also one of the B complex)	Water-soluble
Found in:	egg yolk, liver, kidney, wheat germ, nuts, oats, brewer's yeast/yeast extract.	
Benefits:	metabolism of fats; synthesis of glucose when diet is low in carbohydrates.	
Effects of Deficiency:	very rare in humans.	

Folic Acid	(vitamin B9, foliate, vitamin Bc, pteroylglutamic acid) Water-soluble	
Found in:	liver, kidney, meat, green vegetables, fresh fruit, brewer's yeast/yeast extract, wheat germ, pulses. Recommended daily amount: 0.3mg.	
Benefits:	proper functioning of vitamin B12; formation of red blood cells; metabolism of proteins, fats and carbohydrates.	
Effects of Deficiency:	lack of vitamin B12; anaemia; fatigue; weakness; shortness of breath; irritability; insomnia; forgetfulness, confusion.	

Vitamin Supplementation

If you are in good health and your diet is well-balanced, vitamin supplements are not normally needed. Indeed, an excess of some vitamins can be just as dangerous as a deficiency. Those vitamins that are fat-soluble, and particularly vitamins A and D, can build up in the body to toxic levels. If you do take supplements, be sure to keep to the recommended dosage. When buying vitamins, go to a reputable health shop or supplier and ask for advice before purchasing any supplement.

There are times when supplementation may be necessary: during pregnancy, when taking contraceptive medication, during the menopause, during old age, vegetarians, vegans, people taking part in competitive sports, those who drink a lot of alcohol, smokers, when convalescing after illness.

WARNING: It is important to consult your GP or specialist before embarking on a programme of vitamin and/or mineral supplementation.

Minerals - Essential Traces

The human body contains over twenty essential minerals. These are chemical elements found mostly in non-living matter, but which are present in small proportions in living things. Like vitamins, they are needed for the body's chemistry to work properly. A diet lacking in vital minerals or anything that prevents them from being absorbed can lead to deficiency diseases, and, in the severest cases, death.

Calcium and phosphorus are present in the body in larger quantities than other minerals. Calcium accounts for about two percent of our body weight and is found mostly in bones and teeth. Phosphorus accounts for about one and a half percent of body weight, and again is found mainly in the bones and teeth.

Iron is also vital to our health but it only forms about point zero zero six percent of body weight. About half of this is used in the haemoglobin of the red blood cells. Iron forms part of the pigment haem which gives the cells their colour. Combined with the protein globin this forms the haemoglobin molecule. This has the unique ability to combine reversibly with oxygen to form oxyhaemoglobin, and is the means by which the gas is carried from the lungs to the body tissues. There it combines with glucose and other fuels to produce energy for essential metabolic processes. Some elements are needed in very minute quantities; these we call trace elements.

The amount of a mineral needed by our body varies with age and circumstance. Generally, children require less than adults, but those under seventeen years old need more calcium than adults. Women need more iron than men, and pregnant women and nursing mothers need more iron and calcium. Some minerals can create problems if taken in too large a quantity. Sodium, for example, if taken in excess is thought to contribute to high blood pressure in some people. Salt (sodium chloride) is already present in many manufactured foods to add taste. It's therefore vital to restrict your intake and always read the labels on any purchased foods. On the whole, a healthy, well balanced diet will provide most of the minerals you require.

Selenium is an exception to the rule. It is estimated that most people in the United Kingdom only get about twenty percent of the recommended daily amount of this mineral in their diet. To get the correct daily dose of selenium, it is wise to take a supplement tablet first thing in the morning or last thing at night with water. Your local health shop will usually sell this supplement in the form of a tablet containing selenium combined with vitamin A, C and E. These three vitamins work with selenium as a very good antioxidant combination to purge our bodies of free radicals.

Modern processed foods are not the best providers of minerals. For example, refined foods have depleted amounts of potassium, chromium, selenium and calcium in them. In order to get our recommended daily amounts of most minerals, it is important to eat fresh, wholesome foods.

Vital Minerals

Calcium	
Found in:	dairy products, hard tap water, fish (especially sardines, pilchards and other fish whose bones can be eaten) watercress, fortified cereals, white flour and its products.
Benefits:	growth and maintenance of healthy bones and teeth; several essential processes including nerve functioning, muscle contraction and blood clotting.
Effects of deficiency:	very rare. Its uptake is facilitated by vitamin D, and deficiency of the vitamin may cause rickets in children and osteomalacia (equivalent of rickets in adults).
Iron	
Found in:	red meat, kidney, liver, pulses, dried apricots and figs, cocoa, fortified white flour and products, fortified breakfast cereals, nuts (especially almonds).
Benefits:	healthy blood function; distribution of oxygen and removal of carbon dioxide and other waste products from body tissues by haemoglobin.
Deficiency:	anaemia.
Extreme cases:	depression of immune system.
Chromium	
Found in:	unrefined and unprocessed foods, but especially whole-grain flour, cereals and products, fresh fruits, nuts, liver, kidney, beef, brewer's yeast.
Benefits:	metabolism and storage of fats and sugars; functioning of skeletal muscles; partial control of body's immune system.
Deficiency:	very rare, but may cause irritability, confusion, weakness, and depression.

Cobalt	
Found in:	meat, liver, kidney, eggs.
Benefits:	essential component of vitamin B12.
Deficiency:	lack of vitamin B12 which leads to pernicious anaemia, weak muscles, bowel disorders, nerve disorders.

Copper	
Found in:	most foods, but especially shellfish (particularly oysters), nuts, cocoa, liver, kidney, brewer's yeast, tap water supplied through copper pipes.
Benefits:	functioning of many enzymes; red blood cell formation; bone growth.
Deficiency:	very rare, but may cause low white blood cell count; changes in hair colour and texture (not normal greying); diarrhoea.

Fluorine	
Found in:	fluoridated tap water, toothpastes, tea, sardines and pilchards whose bones are eaten, cereals, meat.
Benefits:	contributes to the health of bones and teeth.
Deficiency:	dental caries; osteoporosis.
Excess:	fluorosis-mottling and discolouration of the teeth; calcification of ligaments; increased density of bones in spine, pelvis and limbs.

Iodine	
Found in:	iodized table salt, seafood including seaweed (kelp), meat, fruit and vegetables grown where soils contain iodine.
Benefits:	production in the thyroid gland of hormones that control metabolism, and therefore healthy growth and development.
Deficiency:	goitre; drop in metabolic rate, leading to drowsiness, lethargy, fatigue, increased weight; deficiency in pregnancy and from birth can lead to cretinism.

Magnesium	
Found in:	most foods, but especially green vegetables, wholemeal flour, cereals and products, milk, eggs, meat, nuts (especially peanuts), pulses, shellfish.
Benefits:	healthy bones and teeth; proper functioning of muscles, nerves, metabolic enzymes, and vitamins B1 and B12.
Deficiency:	loss of appetite; nausea; weakness; anxiety; muscle cramps and tremors; insomnia; rapid or irregular heart beat; hypoglycaemia; premenstrual tension.

Manganese	
Found in:	many foods, but especially wholegrain cereals, nuts, tea, pulses, avocados.
Benefits:	control of growth; the functioning of many enzymes, nerves and muscles; strong, healthy bones.

Molybdenum	
Found in:	many foods, but especially buckwheat, barley, oats, liver, pulses.
Benefits:	prevention of dental caries; iron metabolism; male sexual function.
Deficiency:	increased dental caries; impotence. In extreme cases: irregular heartbeat; coma.

Phosphorus	
Found in:	nearly all foods, but especially high protein foods such as meat, dairy products, pulses.
Benefits:	healthy bones; conversion and storage of energy in all cells; muscle function; function of some enzymes; the intestinal absorption of some foods.
Deficiency:	loss of appetite; weakness; stiff joints; central nervous system disorders; respiratory failure.
Excess:	can prevent intestinal absorption of calcium, iron, magnesium and zinc.

Potassium	
Found in:	most foods, but especially fresh fruit, vegetables, meat, wholemeal flour, cereals and products.
Benefits:	maintenance of body's balance of fluids, especially water; maintenance of body's acid-alkali balance; functioning of nerves and muscles.
Deficiency:	vomiting; abdominal distension; muscular weakness, drowsiness; pins and needles; loss of appetite; low blood pressure; thirst.
Extreme cases:	paralysis, coma.
Excess:	may be dangerous for people with some heart conditions - consult your doctor.

Selenium	
Found in:	unrefined foods, especially wholegrain flour, cereals and products, seafood, egg yolk, liver, kidney, brewer's yeast, garlic.
Benefits:	healthy liver function; with vitamin E, selenium is an antioxidant and detoxifies elements such as cadmium, lead and mercury; the proper functioning of red and white blood cells.
Deficiency:	cardiovascular disease, possibly infant cot death and some types of anaemia.

Sodium	
Found in:	common salt (sodium chloride), baking powder, most foods, especially cured meats, smoked fish, milk, tinned meats, tinned vegetables, bakery products.
Deficiency:	may accompany dehydration, which causes low blood pressure.
Excess:	oedema; hypertension (high blood pressure); heart disorders; some kidney complaints; in babies: diarrhoea and dehydration.

Sulphur	
Found in:	animal proteins, vegetable proteins, meat, dairy products, pulses.
Benefits:	normal protein synthesis; strong hair; nails; skin.

Water	
	This is our most important nutrient. Over three-quarters of the body's weight is water. Together with air, water is vital to life. We can survive for weeks without food, but only a few days without water.
Benefits:	it is a solvent in the digestive process; removes body wastes; regulates the body's temperature; keeps all bodily functions working; prevents constipation.
Effects of deficiency:	dehydration.
Severe:	death.

Zinc	
Found in:	most foods, but especially liver and red meat, egg yolk, dairy produce, wholegrain flour, cereals and products, seafood (particularly oysters).
Benefits:	functioning of many enzymes and thus normal growth and development; the release of insulin and of vitamin A; healthy reproduction; the healing of cuts and wounds.
Deficiency:	slow physical, mental and sexual development; infertility and the slow healing of wounds.

Summary

- Additives and processing agents rob our foods of vital elements.
- We are what we eat. Therefore we must choose healthy, fresh foods.
- Our needs differ depending on age, way of life, metabolic rate and genetic make-up.
- Foods provide carbohydrates, proteins, fats, vitamins, minerals and fibre.
- Carbohydrates, are required in relatively large quantities, and proteins and fats in slightly lesser quantities.
- Carbohydrates are energy givers that fuel our body.
- Proteins repair and build.
- Fats store energy and cushion our organs.
- A daily intake of fibre is essential for correct cleansing, absorption and evacuation of toxins from our bodies.
- The main sources of fibre are vegetables, cereals and grain products.
- Vitamins and minerals in small doses are essential to help the body function correctly.
- Vitamins are vital to the efficient chemical functions of life.
- Minerals, like vitamins, play a vital role in building bones and tissues.
- Minerals are usually found in inanimate materials.
- It is important when having a meal to relax and chew the food thoroughly.

Chapter Seven

Aromatherapy: The Healing Power Of Plants

Beauty is a subtle hint, of some essence far beyond,
Its objects of reflection, like sunbeams upon a pond.

WARNING: All information in this chapter is for the use of people of sixteen years of age onwards. Aromatherapy can be used in specialised ways for children, but it is advisable to seek the advice of a reputable aromatherapist before embarking on any such therapy.

Vital Creative Life Force

On our planet, every living thing has a creative life force. From this invisible centre or soul come radiations of individuality. This creative life force cannot be seen or touched and even when we are ill that same life force gives us the strength and ability to recover.

Plants' Vital Forces

Plants have their own vital forces. Each species has its own range of frequencies of life vibrations. Many plant frequencies correspond with healthful ranges within human bands. The life force within plants is as invisible as within humans. However, all plants contain essential oil, and it is said that within this essential oil, sometimes less than point zero one percent of the plant, lies the very essence of its life. Essential oils are said to be the hormones of the plant. This is not hard to believe, because the hormones that we individually produce during our lifetime would not fill a tablespoon, yet without them we would not exist.

There is evidence that extraction of aromatic substances by distillation was carried out in Mesopotamia over five thousand years ago. In ancient Egypt, China and other civilisations plants were used for making exotic perfumes and medicines. In the books of wisdom of India, the *Vedas* (dating back over four thousand years), there are instructions for the use of herbs, aromatic oils and plants for medicinal purposes. There are records in the Bible, dating back to at least two thousand BC, of plants and their oils being used in the treatment of illness and for religious purposes. Here in the twentieth century we are only re-discovering the great value of aromatherapy.

Aromatherapy primarily makes use of the sense of smell. The area of the brain associated with smell (the olfactory centre) is very closely connected with the limbic system of the brain, which is concerned with our basic drives such as hunger, thirst, and sex drive, and also our most subtle responses such as emotion, memory, creativity and intuition. This area also connects with the hypothalamus which controls the entire hormonal system. It does this by influencing the pituitary body, the master gland. Because of this, odours are able to influence emotional and physical aspects of our being.

Medical Use Of Plant Extracts
Although essential oils are exotic, they do offer medicinal applications. Some of them have psychotherapeutic applications, relieving stress-related problems such as depression, anxiety, insomnia and even pre-menstrual syndrome. Other essential oils have powerful anti-microbial agents within them rivalling antibiotic drugs in their effectiveness. Certainly, aromatherapy is one of the many ways in which the vibrational forces of nature can be made use of in healing.

Odours can also stimulate memory. Smelling the delicious odours of your favourite dish as it is cooking in the kitchen can make your mouth water. Smells can also stimulate mind-pictures and memories. Just for a moment imagine a rose, and imagine its fragrance.

Aromatherapy In Present Times

A Frenchman, Rene Gatefosse, coined the word *aromatherapy*. He was working in his laboratory one day making a perfume when he badly burnt his hand. He plunged it into the nearest bowl of liquid. This happened to be a bowl of essential oil of lavender. His hand healed very quickly, and even though the burns had been severe, there was very little scarring. Being a chemist, Gatefosse was impressed by the antiseptic and healing qualities of this oil. He subsequently researched into the healing properties of other essential oils.

Another Frenchman, Dr Jean Valnet, added to this research whilst working as a surgeon in the Second World War. Since the war, aromatherapy has continued to develop in different ways in different countries. Now in The United Kingdom, with the increasing interest in holistic approaches to healing, aromatherapy is becoming increasingly popular. As mentioned earlier, essential oils were extracted from various plants by a process of distillation. Today this method has been improved upon but it is still the main way of extraction.

The cost of each oil is determined by the rarity of the plant, the difficulties of extraction, and the amount of plant material required to extract sufficient oil. For example, to gain twenty millimetres of essential oil of neroli it takes at least ten sacks of orange blossom. Hence the price of true essential oil of neroli is very expensive.

There are about three hundred different pure essential oils now available. Most of them can be purchased from health stores or by mail order. Most common ailments can be effectively treated with only a few oils. It's important when buying your oils that you check that they are one hundred percent pure essential oil. This must be printed on the label on the bottle. Also check with your supplier that they are the finest quality oils.

CAUTION: Essential oils are volatile, and some are also toxic and dangerous if used improperly. They need to be stored in a cool, dark place. They should come in dark glass bottles.

WARNING: Avoid purchasing synthetic oils which often smell nice but have little or no therapeutic value.

Notes

Oils come in three main bands which are called `notes'. These are top, middle and base. Some oils fall between these categories and are therefore classified as Base/middle or top/middle. The qualities of each note are:

Top notes: The fastest-acting, quickest to evaporate, most stimulating and uplifting to mind and body.

Middle notes: Moderately volatile. Primarily affect the functions of the body, e.g., digestion, menstruation and the general metabolism of the body.

Base notes: Slower to evaporate (if mixed with top note oil, they can help to `hold back' the volatility of that oil). Base notes are the most sedating and relaxing.

Synergies

Dr. Jean Valnet and other pioneers discovered that, when blended, certain essential oils became more powerful than when used singly - the whole becoming greater than the sum of its equal parts. This was particularly noticeable with the anti-bacterial action of essences. A blend of clove, thyme, lavender and peppermint, for example, is far more powerful than might be expected of the blend taking into account the combined chemical constituents of the oils. Up to five oils may be blended in this way: any more in one mixture, curiously, will start to deplete their effectiveness. This blending of several oils not only gives a mixture that can be a wonderful synergy, but will also effectively treat more than one condition at the same time. When making blends for treatments, it is very advantageous to include at least one oil from each note within the mixture. In this way the overall effective time period of the benefits can be substantially extended.

Application

The oils can be applied in several ways including inhalation, foot baths, baths, compresses and massage.

Inhalation: one of the simplest ways to inhale essential oils is simply to put a few drops on a tissue, paper hand-towel or handkerchief and gently breathe in from it. Another way to inhale is to get a bowl with about one hundred millilitre of boiling water in it. Put ten drops of the required essential oil to the water. Now put a towel over your head and the basin. Breathe in deeply (if possible through your nose) until you can no longer smell the scent. In the case of colds etc., repeat this treatment about 3 times a day.

WARNING: The above treatments are not suitable for asthmatics.

Foot baths: take a bowl of hand-hot water with eight to ten drops of essential oil. Keep a kettle of just-boiled water to hand to be added to the water as it cools. Put your feet in the bowl for about ten minutes, moving them around occasionally. When you have finished, wrap your feet in a dry towel for a few more minutes. If you wish, you can finish off the treatment nicely by giving a gentle massage to the your feet and lower legs with a massage oil containing some of the same oils used for the bath.

Baths: draw your bath of hand-hot water. Then add up to eight drops to half a bath of water. If you prefer your bath three quarters full, you may add up to ten drops of your chosen essential oil blend. Then get into your bath and bathe as usual, occasionally turning on your tummy whilst breathing in the aromatic steam. After a few moments it is likely that you will lose the smell. It doesn't matter, the smell will still be there - it's just that your mind has got used to it. Stay in the bath for a minimum of ten minutes to get the full benefits.

The conditions that will benefit from these baths are: arthritis, rheumatism, nervous tension, headaches, coughs, colds, circulatory problems and fluid retention, to name just a few.

Compresses and Massage: these treatments are more complex than the above and so are outside the scope of this present chapter. For those of you who wish to know more about aromatherapy, I have included a book-list at the back of this book.

Some useful oils for home use:

Top Notes

BERGAMOT	Citrus Bergamia
Source:	rind of small orange-like fruit native of Italy.
Aroma:	spicy citrus.
Blends well with:	geranium, lavender, ylang-ylang and most other oils.
Uses:	anti-depressant, uplifting, balancing.
Helpful for:	boils, cold sores, colic, cystitis, fevers, flatulence, oily skin conditions, pre-menstrual syndrome, sore throat, tonsillitis (3 to 4 drops in a cup of warm water 3 times daily), urinary infections.
CAUTION:	never use on skin before sunbathing as it can cause pigmentation. Always use in low concentrations.
EUCALYPTUS	Eucalyptus Globulus
Source:	Australian tall tree.
Aroma:	camphoraceous.
Blends well with:	lavender, lemon, sandalwood.
Uses:	antiseptic; very effective for respiratory disorders, colds, catarrh, cystitis.
Helpful for:	lowering excess blood sugar levels, fevers, 'flu, hayfever, head-lice, measles, migraine, neuralgia, rheumatism, scarlet fever, sinusitis, sprains, throat infections, skin ulcers, wounds, insect repellent.

LEMON	Citrus Limonum
Source:	expression of the lemon rind. The lemon tree is native to the Mediterranean.
Aroma:	clear, sharp and refreshing. The essential oil does not keep well; use within nine months of purchase.
Blends well with:	most essential oils, especially eucalyptus, geranium, lavender, tea-tree, ylang-ylang.
Uses:	fortifying to the nervous system.
Helpful for:	arthritis, anaemia, asthma, cellulite, chilblains, colds, congestion in tissues, conjunctivitis, diabetes, 'flu, fluid retention, gallstones, high blood pressure, insect bites and stings, rheumatism, sore throats, verrucae, warts, wounds, insect repellent.
CAUTION:	do not use on the skin prior to sunbathing - it may cause permanent pigmentation.

NIAOULI	Melaleuca Viridiflora
Source:	distillation from leaves and twigs from Australia, Tasmania and the East Indies.
Uses:	anxiety, bronchitis, depression.
Helpful for:	lowering excess blood sugar levels, fevers, 'flu, hayfever, head-lice, measles, migraine, neuralgia, rheumatism, scarlet fever, sinusitis, sprains, throat infections, skin ulcers, wounds, insect repellent.
Note:	in its countries of origin this oil is used in place of lavender.

TEA-TREE	Melaleuca Alternifolia
Source:	leaves and twigs from tree native only to Australia.
Aroma:	medicinal, slightly pungent.
Blends well with:	only mixes well with eucalyptus, lemon or lavender.
Uses:	powerful antiseptic, antibiotic, anti-viral, anti-fungal, immune system stimulant.
Helpful for:	acne, athletes foot, cold sores, colds, coughs, dandruff, 'flu, insect bites, stings, ringworm, thrush, verrucae, warts, wounds, shock and hysteria.

Middle Notes

CAMOMILE ROMAN	Anthemis Noblis
Source:	floral daisy like herb.
Aroma:	dry and slightly sweet.
Blends well with:	geranium, lavender and ylang-ylang.
Uses:	sedative, anti-inflammatory.
Helpful for:	acne, allergies (skin and respiratory), boils, chilblains, cold sores, colic, colitis, eczema, indigestion, insomnia, menopausal problems, period pain, pre-menstrual syndrome, psoriasis, rheumatism, general skin care (most skins), sprains, stomach cramps, inflammation of joints, swellings, wounds.
CAUTION:	this is a very powerful essential oil, only use in extremely low concentrations especially when treating allergies.

GERANIUM	Pelargonium Odorantissium
Source:	plant native to Reunion, Madagascar and Guinea.
Aroma:	freshly floral and sweet.
Blends well with:	bergamot, ylang-ylang and most other essential oils.
Uses:	balancing, relaxing, stimulation.
Helpful for:	cellulite, diabetes (like eucalyptus it can lower blood sugar levels), fluid retention, mouth ulcers, neuralgia, ringworm, shingles, thrush, sore throats, wounds.
CAUTION:	not to be used during pregnancy or whilst breast-feeding. Can occasionally be too stimulating for a few sensitive individuals.
JUNIPER	Juniperus Communis
Source:	distillation of the berries from the evergreen shrub native to the northern hemisphere. There is also an inferior grade oil obtained from the wood.
Aroma:	clear, slightly peppery with a resinous overtone.
Blends well with:	citrus essences, geranium, lavender, rosemary, and sandalwood.
Uses:	primarily tonic, cleansing and diuretic.
Helpful for:	absence of periods outside pregnancy, arthritis, cellulite, coughs, cystitis, fluid retention, gout, haemorrhoids, nervous tension, oily skin conditions, respiratory infections, rheumatism, weeping eczema.
CAUTION:	it is important to differentiate between juniper berry and juniper - the latter is usually the inferior grade. The oil should be labelled 'juniper berry'. Medicinal properties are reduced in the oil obtained from the wood.
Warning:	do not use either of these juniper oils during pregnancy.

LAVENDER	Lavandula Officinalis
Source:	lavender flower tops. Native to the Mediterranean countries.
Aroma:	refreshingly floral.
Blends well with:	bergamot, camomile, ylang-ylang and most other essential oils.
Uses:	regulates the central nervous system. Refreshing and relaxing.
Helpful for:	abscess, acne, athletes foot, anxiety, bad breath, boils, bronchitis, burns, chilblains, colds, coughs, cuts, cystitis, dandruff, depression, dermatitis, earache, eczema, fainting, flatulence, fluctuating moods, head-lice, high blood pressure, infectious inflammation, illness, insect bites, palpitations, stings, insomnia, laryngitis, lymphatic congestion, migraine, muscular aches and pains, nervous tension, period (scanty and painful), pre-menstrual syndrome, skin care (all types of skin), sprains and hair tonic.
ROSEMARY	Rosemarinus Officinalis
Source:	distillation of the flowering tops of the herb. Native to Spain.
Aroma:	warm, sharp and camphoraceous.
Blends well with:	basil, citrus oils, juniper, lavender.
Uses:	primarily a stimulating essence to both body and mind.
Helpful for:	arthritis, bronchitis, burns, colds, dandruff, 'flu, hair loss, headache, head-lice, high cholesterol, indigestion, low blood pressure, mental fatigue, migraine, nervous debility, palpitations, rheumatism, skin care (especially oily skin conditions), wounds.
CAUTION:	not to be used during pregnancy as it may be too stimulating. If used continuously over a long period of time it may provoke convulsions in prone subjects.

Base Notes

GINGER	Zingiber Officinale
Source:	distillation of the underground stems (rhizomes) of the plant native to China.
Aroma:	not as pleasantly pungent as the freshly grated root. Unfortunately, the intense heat of distillation tends to distort the aroma.
Blends well with:	citrus oils and patchouli. Use sparingly, otherwise its powerful aroma will dominate the blends you make.
Uses:	warming to both body and mind; a reputed aphrodisiac; helpful for arthritis, chilblains, colds, cramp, fibrositis, 'flu, muscle sprain, muscular aches and pains, nervous tension, anxiety, poor circulation, rheumatism, travel sickness, as a gargle for sore throats (1 or 2 drops in a cup of luke-warm water, stir well).
CAUTION	not suitable for those with sensitive skin. Avoid using during pregnancy as it may be too stimulating.
NEROLI	Citrus Aurantium, Bigaradia
Source:	distillation of the blossom from the bitter orange tree native to southern Europe.
Aroma:	a sweetish dry scent, not at all `citrusy'.
Blends well with:	camomile, citrus essences, geranium, juniper, lavender and sandalwood.
Uses:	primarily anti-depressant and sedative with a slightly hypnotic effect; a reputed aphrodisiac.
Helpful with:	nervous tension, palpitations, insomnia, shock, hysteria, and emotional disturbances. Also useful for skin care (suitable for most skins).

PATCHOULI	Pogosstemon Patchoule
Source:	distillation of the dried leaves of a herb native to the Far East and West Indies.
Aroma:	an earthy Eastern scent which becomes sweeter once the sour element of the oil has worn off.
Blends well with:	citrus essences, geranium, ginger, lavender and several other essences.
Uses:	primarily antibiotic, anti-fungal, anti-depressant and fortifying. A reputed aphrodisiac.
Helpful for:	acne, anxiety, depression, cellulite, cracked skin, athlete's foot, fluid retention, fevers, thinning hair and sores.
SANDALWOOD	Santalum Album
Source:	heartwood of a parasitic Indian tree.
Aroma:	soft, woody and sweet.
Blends well with:	many other essential oils including the citrus varieties and ylang-ylang.
Uses:	relief of nervous tension, breathing problems, skin problems. A pleasant aphrodisiac relaxant.
Helpful for:	acne, bronchitis, catarrh, coughs, cystitis, depression, diarrhoea, insomnia, laryngitis, PMS, skin tonic for oily, dry and aging skins.
YLANG-YLANG	Cananga Odorata
Source:	flower petals of native tree of Indonesia.
Aroma:	sweet fragrance
Blends well with:	camomile, bergamot, geranium, lavender, and sandalwood.
Uses:	healing distressing emotions, wonderful anti-depressant and aphrodisiac.
Helpful for:	anxiety, depression, high blood pressure, tension, palpitations, PMS.
NOTE:	The finest quality of this oil is usually listed as ylang-ylang extra. Inferior grades known as ylang-ylang 2, 3, or cananga are also available.

A few useful formulas for using in your bath:

Condition	Oil-drops	Oil-drops	Oil-drops
arthritis and joints	Lavender 3	Camomile 2	Rosemary 3
rheumatism	Eucalyptus 6	Juniper 3	Rosemary 3
bronchitis	Eucalyptus 6	Sandalwood 2	
chilblains	Lemon 3	Lavender 3	
head-cold	Eucalyptus 4	Tea-tree 5	
dermatitis	Geranium 4	Juniper 3	Lavender 3
eczema	Bergamot 3	Geranium 4	Lavender 3
high blood pressure	Lavender 5	Ylang-ylang 5	
insomnia	Camomile 2	Juniper 4	Ylang-ylang 4
stress	Niaouli 2	Lavender 4	Ylang-ylang 4
nervous tension	Juniper 2	Lavender 4	Ylang-ylang 4
tonic and refreshing	Ginger 4	Eucalyptus 3	Tea-tree 3

To become efficient in the use of essential oils, it is important that you experiment in blending the oils yourself and making notes of the effects. Eventually you will find just the right blends for your particular pleasure and enjoyment.

Summary

- Every living thing on our planet has vibrating within it a creative life force which cannot be seen or touched.
- Plants have their own vital forces which radiate from the essential oil contained within them.
- These essential oils are usually less that point zero one percent of each plant.
- For thousands of years human kind has been extracting these essential oils from the plants.
- The therapeutic benefits of using the essential oils in healing is immense.
- Over the last century the use of aromatic oils has become more popular. It is now called `aromatherapy': a name given to it by a Frenchman Rene Gatefosse.
- There are about three hundred aromatic oils now available. Most are volatile and some are dangerous when used incorrectly.
- When essential oils are blended together, an effective synergy occurs.
- Oils may be applied through inhalation, foot baths, baths, compresses and massage.
- When choosing your oils always check the quality. Store them in a dark, cool place.

Chapter Eight

Human Energy Centres

Nature works in cycles, which are circles of a kind;
No starting point, no ending place, revolving all the time;
The Universe its Galaxies, with stars and planets too;
Move endlessly in cyclic ways, to improve and evolve ever new;

And even inside atoms, infinite vortices will play;
The game of flying round with speed, and in one place won't stay;
whilst in our world of seasons, birth and death fulfil the round;
In every form and living thing, in air; in sea; on ground.

We are made of the same components as the universe, namely: Earth, Water, Fire, Air, Psyche/Soul and Space or Ether. A seventh component is totally outside our understanding - we refer to this as Spirit, Cause or God. Every human being traverses many levels of being, each with its own quality and vibrations of energy. These levels or bodies ascend in subtlety from the physical level through to the spiritual level. Each connects and has vortices through which energy flows both in and out. These energy exchanges are said to occur in areas and on levels which correspond to the position of glands and organs within the physical body.

In the Orient these lines of force and areas of exchange are described as meridians, and the primary points as acupuncture points. (Acupuncture is the art of correcting and redirecting energy flow to allow balance within an organism.)

The Chakras

In India, the Sages referred to vortices as chakras - wheels. There are said to be thousands of these in each human being. In this chapter we are only concerned with the seven main or primary vortices or chakras.

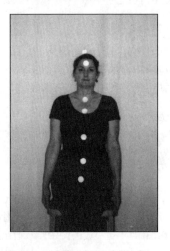

Sahasrara-Padma	- crown
Ajna	- brow
Visuddha	- thyroid
Anahata	- heart
Manipura	- solar plexus
Svadhisthana	- sacral
Muladhara	- base chakra

Sahasrara-Padma - Crown

Located within the crown of the head, this externalizes as the pineal gland and governs the upper brain and right eye. It is the point of connection or unity with Divine Spirit - Brahman. Its colour is brilliant violet, brighter than sunlight. Its primal sound is AUM - the first sound of the universe, the basis of all creation. It is said to be the first sound ever heard and to be the parent of all sounds.

Ajna - Brow/Third Eye

Situated in the centre of the forehead just above the eyebrows. Often referred to as the third eye. It externalizes as the pituitary gland. It governs the lower brain and nervous system, ears, nose and the left eye - the eye of personality. Its colour is indigo. Its element is Spirit. It is the centre of inner sight - visualisation. Its balancing sound is OM or sometimes said to be AH. Its number is two.

Visuddha - Thyroid/Hollow Of Throat

Residing in the hollow of the throat, just below the thyroid gland, this governs the lungs, vocal chords, bronchia and metabolism. It is the chakra of communication, speech, expression, self-worth and judgement both of the self and others. Its colour is a dark velvety blue. Its shape is oval. Its element is Ether - the unified field. Its balancing sound is HAM. Its number is sixteen.

Anahata - Heart/Thymus

This chakra lies near to and just above the human heart in line with the spine. It has links with the thymus gland, and is said to govern the heart, blood and circulatory system, and also influence the immune and endocrine systems. It is said to be the temple of the soul and the centre of universal and unconditional love. Its colour is emerald green with a sparkling six-pointed star of blue light within it (an alternative colour is pink). Its element is soul. Its balancing sound is YAM. Its number is twelve.

Manipura - Solar Plexus

This chakra resides in the area of the solar plexus. It is the centre of power and physical energy. It externalizes as the pancreas and is said to have influence over the actions of the liver, spleen, stomach, gall bladder and aspects of the nervous system. It is the centre for emotional sensitivities and issues of personal power. Its colour is yellow with a red down-pointing triangle of glowing light within it. Its element is Fire. Its balancing sound is RAM. Its number is 10.

Svadhisthana - Sacral

This chakra resides just below the navel within the centre of the body. It is linked to ovaries in women and testes in men. Often referred to as the Sacral Chakra, it is the sexual vortex and the battery of human life. It governs emotions and creativity, and is closely linked with attitudes in relationships, sex and reproduction. Its element is Water. Its colour is orange with a silver crescent moon of light within it. Its balancing sound is VAM. Its number is six.

Muladhara - Route/Base

This is the root centre situated at the base of the spine, the perineum. Its purpose is survival and is described as the chakra that governs understanding of the physical dimension. Here is initiated the `fight and flight' responses. It is related to the adrenals, and is said to govern the kidneys and the spinal column. It is usually perceived as glowing red in colour, with a yellow square within it. Its element is Earth. Its balancing sound is LAM. Its number is four.

Kundilini - Vital Force (Female Serpent Power)

Kundilini is said to reside in the base chakra, coiled three and a half times. As we develop and move forward intuitively towards higher understandings and states of consciousness, the Kundilini naturally rises up through each chakra, enlivening and activating the qualities at each level. The energy passes through psychic channels. There are said to be as many as seventy-two thousand psychic channels or Nadis within each of us. Here we will discuss only the three main ones. These have been named Ida, Pingala and Sushumna.

Ida

This is the channel or route which female energy uses to travel up the left side of the spine. The left nostril has influence upon this channel or flow. The Ida energy is called Moon or female energy.

Pingala

This is the channel which carries male energy down the right side of the spine. The right nostril can influence this channel or flow. The Pingala energy is called Sun or male energy.

Ida and Pingala

Both these channels make connections with each chakra centre along the spine. It is often suggested that they coil around, one clockwise and one anti-clockwise, as they pass from one chakra to the next.

Sushumna

This channel runs up vertically joining the chakras. It corresponds to the hollow part of the spinal column. It starts at the base of the spine and goes up to the medulla oblongata, and then on up to the third eye. It is only activated when both the Ida and Pingala are open.

Dangers

There are many theories about raising the Kundilini energy. It can be a very dangerous task and I would advise against any form of dabbling. Imbalances in chakras can cause disorders, illness and discomforts both emotional and physical. These conditions usually occur within the areas attributed to each chakra. The resultant illness is often reflected within the glands and organs in the area of the particular chakra which is blocked, underactive or overactive.

Energy Balancing Exercise One

It's possible, without dabbling, to get your energies nicely balanced. Here is a very simple yet effective exercise:

1. Get yourself comfortable. Spend about two minutes sitting comfortably doing *The Balancing Breath* exercise. (Instructions in Chapter Two.)

2. Now lie down comfortably on your back. Support your head on a soft cushion or pillow.

3. Breathe gently and easily with your body loose and limp, and your arms alongside you on the floor, hands open and loose. Be sure that you will be undisturbed for about twenty minutes or so.

4. Close your eyes and visualise, in any way you like, a yellow square or cube of light glowing in your mind's eye.

5. Breathe a few gentle breaths whilst establishing this vision.

6. Now see or feel, in any way that is real for you, this yellow square sliding down your spine until it reaches the base. Here feel its gentle glow. Stay with this vision for some moments feeling very comfortable until you are ready to move on to the next image.

7. See in your mind's eye a silver crescent moon lying on its back sparkling with beautiful radiance. Breathe gently to establish this vision.

8. Feel that moon slide down your spine until it reaches a position just about two inches below your navel. Enjoy it glowing here within your body. Take a few moments in this experience.

9. Now in your mind's eye imagine, see in any way you can, a brightly glowing, down-turned triangle. Just give it time to really appear, and then slowly watch and feel as it slides down your spine and stops at your solar plexus.

10. Feel it energising and balancing you comfortably. Spend a few moments inside this experience.

11. Now it's time to see in your mind's eye a blue glowing six-pointed star. Just allow this vision to establish itself.

12. Breathing gently, be aware of the star slowly moving down until it reaches a position in the centre of your body adjacent to your heart. Here let it give out radiations of healing light.

13. Stay within these feelings for a few moments and then move your attention back to your mind's eye.

14. In the hollow of your throat imagine a velvety, dark blue or black oval of quiescence nestling there, soothing, healing and allowing that area to become soft and somehow loose.

15. Stay with this experience for a few moments.

16. Again return your attention to the mind's eye and here feel and experience a swirling, bright radiance which first appears to be white light but soon emits flickers of brilliant indigo light blending within it.

17. Enjoy this radiance for a while and then move on.

18. Now put your full attention inside the crown of your head and locate a tiny point of luminance, shining brightly like a miniature sun. Notice that the light is a beautiful translucent violet, almost brilliant white at times.

19. Take a little time to become aware of all the glowing lights and their positions as follows: at the base of the spine a bright yellow cube of light; approximately two inches below the navel a shining silver crescent of sparkling light; at the solar plexus a glowing red triangle; at the heart centre a bright blue, six-pointed star of light made up of two inverted merged triangles. In the hollow of the throat a soothing velvety dark blue, almost black, oval of peacefulness; at the brow centre a spiralling bright light flashing indigo; within the crown of your head a violet brilliant shining point of light.

20. Now take a few long, gentle breaths and then imagine the lights from each of these positions travelling upwards and merging with all the other colours, finally at the crown merging and flowing outwards and down through your whole being like waterfalls of soothing white light. Feel your whole body being washed as this cycle continues over and over several times.

21. Now allow the white light to begin to fade and, during this time, rest. Allow yourself five or ten minutes before getting up and returning to your life.

Tips to help you fully benefit from this exercise.

- Have a nice, supportive yet comfortable surface to lie on.
- Do not do this exercise just after a meal. Wait a couple of hours or do it before a meal.
- Do not do this exercise too often. Once or twice a week at the most will give maximum benefits.
- If you are unable to remember the sequence of events record yourself reading through this script. Play some soft music in the background as you make your recording.
- If you don't feel able to make the recording yourself, ask a significant other to do it for you.
- Lie down, listen, stay loose and limp, and breathe easily and effortlessly throughout the session.

Balancing Exercise Two

If the symbols in the last exercise are too difficult for you to visualise, you might find the symbols in this exercise easier to work with. It takes about the same amount of time and offers similar benefits.

1. Close your eyes and visualise, in any way you like, in your mind's eye a ball of rose-red light about the size of a golf ball. See the light glowing. Take a few gentle breaths whilst you strengthen the image and then imagine that ball of light travelling down your spine until it reaches the base.

2. Now imagine that light expanding until it fills your whole body with rose-red light and even surrounds you. Feel yourself almost floating in this healing light. After a few moments imagine the light shrinking back down to its original size and staying there, glowing gently at the base of the spine.

3. Now imagine in your mind's eye an orange ball of light about the size of an orange. Intensify that image, take a few gentle breaths and then feel the ball of light slide down the spine until it reaches a position adjacent to, or just below, your navel.

4. Feel it glowing, see the lovely, orange luminance and feel it expand to encompass all your body, filling you with warm healing light; glowing, soothing, healing light filling and surrounding you.

5. After a few moments allow the light to shrink back down to its original size, glowing there just below the navel.

6. Now in your mind's eye see a lovely, yellow, golden light glowing there and after a few gentle breaths feel that ball of light slide down the spine until it reaches the area of your solar plexus.

7. Here it spins gently and expands until you are aware of being filled with beautiful, sunny, yellow light. Enjoy this for a few moments; feel all your body rejoicing in this lovely healing light.

8. Now allow the light to shrink down until it reaches the size of a basketball and spins there in the solar plexus region.

9. In your mind's eye see or imagine a glowing orb of emerald light about the size of your heart. When you are aware of it take a few gentle breaths.

10. Now be aware of it slowly sliding down the spine and stopping in the centre of the upper chest just above your heart.

11. Here it will glow with a soothing, relaxing feeling, reflecting soothing, healing, emerald rays throughout your whole body, healing and refreshing all the tissues and organs.

12. After a few moments feel the emerald light return to the size of your heart, just glowing there in your upper chest.

13. Now in the hollow of the throat be aware of a lovely, oval, blue light. Feel a gentle, relaxing sensation taking place, a nice, cooling sensation within the throat.

14. Enjoy this feeling for a few moments, breathing gently and easily.

15. Now in your mind's eye, imagine there is a spinning white light in your brow.

16. Feel the gentle sensations as that light radiates white, gentle light; healing, soothing and refreshing your whole body. In this white light occasionally you might be aware of flashes of indigo, subtly blending within that radiance.

17. Finally put your attention into the crown of your head and imagine here a tiny speck of brilliant light just glowing there.

18. Now lie there being aware of the seven lights just glowing and sending out healing sensations all the way through every part of your body; red at the base of the spine; orange just below the navel; yellow in the solar plexus; emerald green at the heart centre; an oval of blue light in the hollow of your throat; a white spiral in the brow; and a brilliant violet light in the crown; soothing, healing, loosening.

19. Now take a few breaths and imagine that each time you are breathing in you are taking in soothing, healing, white light through your nose and filling your body with this lovely energy.

20. Finally, just lie there with your eyes closed for a few more minutes before getting up and continuing with your life.

Tips On How To Use The Exercises

The above exercises can be used whenever you feel low in energy. They can also be used at times when you feel too hyped-up or anxious. They balance the different levels of energy within your being and therefore lead to a nice, level feeling. Other advantages are that they relieve stress and perk up the immune system.

- Before attempting a technique read through the instructions several times and make short notes on the order of colours, positions, shapes and sizes of the symbols.
- When doing the technique, don't concentrate too hard; just get an image or idea of shape and colour as you visualise each of the symbols.
- Either exercise may be audio-recorded and played back, as explained after exercise one.
- Those who are easily excited or have high blood pressure should substitute pink for red; light lemon for orange; and pale yellow for yellow.
- If you have low blood pressure or feel lethargic, spend a little more time during the technique on the first three chakras as this can have an energising effect.
- Do not spend more than a minute's visualisation on each chakra.
- Never do both exercises on the same day. Choose the one you feel most comfortable with and use for several weeks. This way, progress is made.

Chakra Sound Balancing

Earlier I mentioned that each chakra has a sound. They are, from base chakra upwards:

LAM, VAM, RAM, YAM, HAM, AH, AUM.

They can be likened to the notes in a musical scale: DOH, RAY, ME, FAH, SOH, LAH, TEE. Notice that each note is one higher than the one before it. In this exercise you can use the notes of the sound scale with the sounds of the chakras to gain a nice balance within your energy system.

Sound Balancing Exercise

1. Spend a few moments getting comfortable. You can lie down as in the previous exercise or sit comfortably with your spine upright, without any tension.

2. Do *The Balancing Breath* for up to two minutes, with your eyes closed.

3. Now use your hands to locate the seven chakra positions. Ensure that you know where each one is before commencing this technique.

4. Now, as if singing the musical scale, begin singing slowly in ascendance: LAM, VAM, RAM, YAM, HAM, AH, AUM. As you intone each sound, locate the bodily position of each associated chakra lightly with a hand, and imagine that vibration in that chakra area. Eventually, after several daily attempts, you might find yourself actually not only feeling the sound in that area, but having a visual, internal idea of the associated chakra colour and/or symbol as mentioned in the previous exercises. I must stress that this is not a conscious decision: all you are attempting to do here is to use sound in these areas to balance energies.

5. You may do this sequence of sound through once aloud then through again silently, just imagining the sounds. Now do it aloud and then silently for another six rounds.

6. Now rest for a few moments with your eyes open or closed, lying or sitting, whichever you feel most comfortable with.

Maximise The Benefits

*   Chakra sounds are intoned/stretched out; each sound has three syllables joined into one continuous tone. Notice the first two syllables are three times longer that the actual alphabetical letter itself and the last syllable is about five or more times longer. The last syllable is made with both lips together, vibrating like the hum of a bee:

LLLAAAMMMMM; VVVAAAMMMMM; RRRAAAMMMMM; YYYAAAMMMMM; HHHAAAMMMMM; AAAHHHMMM; AAAUUUMMM.

*   During the exercise you may pause at any time between any chakras to breathe as necessary. Then continue, remembering the next higher note as well as the sound.
*   You may alternate between aloud and silent sounds or do the full sequence aloud or silently. You will intuitively find the best way for your personal practice.

Summary

- "Chakra" means wheel or vortice.
- In human beings, chakras are energy centres ascending from the densest, at the base of the spine, up to the finest, within the crown.
- There are said to be seven main chakras: Muladhara - base of spine; Svadhisthana - sacral; Manipura - solar plexus; Anahata - heart/thymus; Visuddha - thyroid; Ajna - brow; Sahasrara-Padma - crown.
- If chakras are unbalanced and receiving or transmitting too much energy or are blocked, illness, either mental, physical or physiological may be a result.
- The illness is usually associated with the malfunction of glands, organs or tissues governed by a particular chakra's energy and position in the body.
- Kundilini vital force lies coiled in the base chakra ready to rise up when awakened.
- The channels for energy running between the chakras are Ida-female-left, Pingala-male-right, and Sushumna running through the centre of the spine from base up to the brow.
- It is dangerous to attempt to artificially raise Kundilini. Dabbling can lead to ill-health.
- The chakras may be brought into balance by using any one of the three exercises mentioned in this chapter.
- These exercises rely on pleasant, easy-to-do visualisation and sound techniques.

Chapter Nine

Youthfulness And Vibrancy

Wisdom is the light of God, the essence of all things;
Without it nothing could exist; no life, no Earth, no Beings.

In the last chapter, I described energy centres and how to bring them into balance. In this chapter, will give you some insight into how this energy can be used within the physical body to awaken dormant and sleeping potential for vibrancy and youthfulness. Ever since human beings first searched for the fountain of youth, this desire has lead to the creation of hormonal preparations, "miracle" skin creams, special rainforest concoctions, pollen extracts, plastic surgery, etc.

It is natural to wish to keep or achieve this status of youthfulness because it is synonymous with so many things that make life exciting and enjoyable - vitality, optimism, lack of illness and disease - in other words, health.

There is an ancient Indian legend of a warrior who roamed the entire world in search of a precious jewel that he had lost. After many years of fruitless searching, he returned to his home village only to have a child point out to him that the very jewel he sought was imbedded in his own forehead. By the same token, I suggest that youthfulness cannot be sought outside, no matter how far you travel and where you search. The secret is within you.

Vital Force

Within you lies the tremendous vital force necessary to continually regenerate your physical organism. This vital force lies within every atom of your being and is extremely active in the early years of your life, but unless it is periodically stimulated and activated it will become less active and more dormant as the years go by. It gradually goes to sleep.

But here is some good news. With a little effort you can awaken and stimulate this dormant vital force once again. This awakening can be encouraged very simply by manipulating your body in such a way that organs, glands, nerves, cells, bones and joints where the vital force lies sleeping are methodically stimulated, nourished, stretched and relaxed.

Exercises For Youthfulness

In this chapter I will outline a simple routine containing stretching exercises, which only take about ten to fifteen minutes daily to complete. These exercises, although easy to do, will allow you to strengthen and recondition your entire body. Regular practice will help maintain relaxation, not only in body but also in mind. You have only to test this programme a few times to accomplish the following:

- Bring into balance all energy centres (chakras).
- Strengthen and recondition your entire body.
- Regain youthful flexibility in spine and limbs.
- Help control and redistribute your weight in accordance with your correct physical structure.
- Remove tension from all parts of your body and mind.
- Remain relaxed under pressure.
- Store and release energy and vital force to be used as needed.
- Heighten resistance to many common disorders.
- Restore grace, balance, poise and self-confidence.
- Awaken the vital force to help gain control of your emotions.
- Improve in every one of your activities.

CAUTION: All the following techniques are dynamic and should be carried out slowly, without any strain. With regular practice you will be able to go further into each position. The body will automatically adjust itself over time without any force being required.

Sitting Forward Stretch

Benefits: relieves tension in the back. Stretches and tones the legs and thigh muscles.

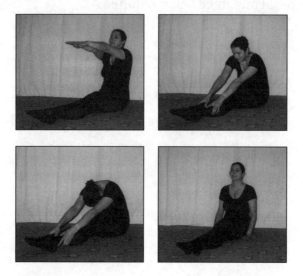

Technique:

1. Sit on the floor, keep both legs together and extended out in front of you.

2. Extend both arms together straight out in front of you at eye level.

3. In slow motion, carefully stretch as far forward as you can and grasp the farthermost part of your legs; this could be the knees, calves, ankles or feet depending on your flexibility. Don't over-stretch.

4. Now, ever so effortlessly, bend the elbows outward and lower yourself forward and downward until you reach a point were you can feel some tension but without strain. Stay still and hold this position for about five seconds.

5. Now, very slowly, raise your trunk and return to the original sitting position.

6. After a few moments, rest. Repeat the exercise.

Important Points

- Never strain. Go only far enough to feel a slight tension. Do not jerk or force anything.

- Keep both legs straight and the backs of both knees touching the floor throughout.

- Bend your elbows out slightly as you draw your head downwards.

- When you reach the extreme position, count the seconds silently.

- You may close your eyes during the exercise if you wish.

Alternate Leg Pull

Benefits: strengthens the shoulders and lumbar region of the back; tightens the muscles of the abdomen and thighs; strengthens the ligaments, muscles and tendons of the legs and feet.

Technique:
1. Sit on the floor with your legs extended straight out in front of you. Keep your feet together and make sure the backs of the knees are in contact with the floor.

2. Bend your right leg at the knee and bring your foot towards you. Take hold of your foot with both hands.

3. Bring the sole of your right foot against the upper inside of your left thigh. Keep the right heel as close in to your groin as possible.

4. Very slowly, bend forward and take hold of the farthermost part of your left leg that you can without straining. This might be your knee, calf, ankle or foot.

5. Bend your elbows outwards slightly and, holding onto your left leg with your hands, pull gently forwards. At the same time, with your neck loose, lower your forehead as close to your left knee as possible. Do not overstretch or strain. Be sure that the back of your left knee is touching the floor all the time. Breathe slowly and easily, with your eyes closed. Remain in this position for about five seconds.

6. Then slide your hands back up the leg towards the top of your thigh, as you slowly raise your trunk to the upright position. Finally putting your hands on the floor at your sides, take a few moments' rest.

7. When you have rested, slowly extend the right leg straight out in front of you. Now bend the left leg at the knee and bring it towards you so that you can take hold of your left foot with both hands. Proceed exactly as in step 3, simply substituting the word `left' for `right' and vice-versa.

Important Points

*   Keep the back of the knee of your outstretched leg touching the floor. Don't worry too much about how far down your leg you are able to hold, as time goes on, each time you do this exercise you will get further down until you will be able to go right down to the foot. The actual stretch is the important component of this exercise.

*   Always aim your forehead down towards your knee; keep your neck limp to assist in this.

*   Breathe slowly throughout the exercise, eyes closed; count the seconds silently.

Backward Bend

Benefits: helps relieve spinal tension; encourages elasticity in the spine; firms and develops chest and bust; tones and strengthens the feet and toes.

Technique:

1. Sit on your heels, with your knees together in front of you. Have the soles of your feet pointing upwards and the tops of your feet in contact with the floor.

2. Put the palms of your hands on the floor, resting at each side of your body.

3. Bit by bit, `walk' back with your hands until you reach a comfortable maximum.

4. Lower your head backwards and push your abdomen and chest upward to form an arch. During this time, remain seated on your heels. Hold this position for about five seconds, counting slowly with eyes closed. Do not fidget; remain absolutely still, breathing gently.

5. Now, slowly lower your abdomen and chest and bring your head back to the upright position. Stay seated on your heels and do not move your hands.

6. Repeat, by dropping your head backwards and slowly pushing upward with your abdomen and chest as described in step 4.

7. Now, come out of the posture by slowly dropping your abdomen and chest and raising your head. Walk forward little by little until you are able to easily raise your trunk from your heels.

8. Next, change the position of your feet by bending your toes so that they now rest on the floor under your feet. Sit on your heels.

9. Now perform the exact movements of steps 2, 3 and 4. Move with care and stop as soon as you begin to feel even the slightest strain. If you find this more difficult than before, put most of your weight on your heels and toes whilst holding the posture for five seconds.

10. Come out of the posture as before, then relax and massage your feet to release any tension.

Important Points
• Stay seated on your heels at all times during the technique.

• Don't forget to let your head drop gently backwards at the appropriate time.

• Keep your arms parallel with your sides and make sure your fingers are pointing behind you.

• When coming out of the posture move your palms forward little by little; no jerky movements.

Twist Arounds

Benefits: removes stiffness; promotes elasticity in the spine; helps to tone up tummy muscles; strengthens feet and legs; promotes balance and good posture in general.

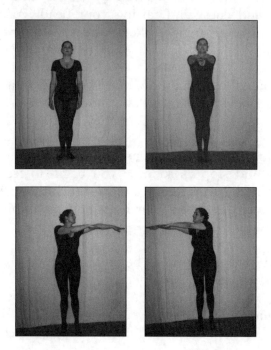

Technique:

1. Stand comfortably with your arms at your sides and with your feet pointing very slightly outwards.

2. Raise your arms from your sides and stretch them straight out in front of you at eye-level, hands touching, palms facing downwards.

3. Stand up on your toes.

4. Keep your eyes trained on the back of your hands as you slowly rotate your trunk to the left. Go as far around to the left as you can without straining. Keep your balance as you stay on your tiptoes. Hold this extreme position for five seconds.

5.   Return slowly to face the front and slowly lower your arms to your sides. Rest for a few moments without moving. Now carry out the identical movements to the right.

6.   Return to the front position and relax as before. Now carry out the whole sequence once more, then rest.

Important Points

*   During the whole exercise stay as high on your toes as possible without overbalancing.

*   Keep your gaze on the back of your hands.

*   Hold your tummy in and your chest out as you circle to the sides.

*   Keep your posture upright.

*   If you lose your balance at any time, come right back to the point where you lost balance and continue.

The Cobra

Benefits: relaxes and tones the vertebrae all the way through the spine; relieves all tension in the back; strengthens the muscles of the chest, back and buttocks; helps improve posture.

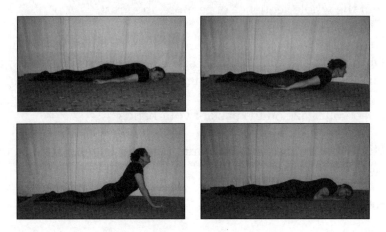

Technique:

1. Lie on your tummy with your face resting on your left cheek and your arms at your sides. Allow your body to go loose and limp; close your eyes.

2. Turn your head so that your forehead rests on the floor.

3. Now slowly raise your head upwards and backwards, using only your neck muscles.

4. Now gently inhale and, with your head held back, slowly raise your trunk from the floor as far as you can using just your back muscles, leaving the lower part of your body from the waist to the toes in contact with the floor.

5. When you have raised your trunk to its comfortable limit, bring your hands in from your sides and place them on the floor below your upper chest with the fingers of both hands pointing slightly inwards towards each other.

6. Now gently press down with both hands. Keep your elbows close in to the body and extend the spine upward.

7. Don't strain as you hold this position for five seconds.

8. At the completion of the count, slowly lower your body, uncurving it as you move back to the starting position.

9. When your forehead touches the floor, pause for a moment and turn your right cheek to rest on the floor (the opposite cheek to the one at the beginning of the exercise).

10. Relax for a few moments then repeat the exercise.

Shoulder Stand

Benefits: improves circulation; relaxes legs and other tense areas; allows any displaced organs to edge back into their correct positions within the body; has a beneficial effect on the thyroid gland.

Technique:

1. Lie on your back with your arms at your sides. Breathe comfortably, and close your eyes.

2. Turn your palms to face the floor and press downwards. Keep your leg muscles tense.

3. Slowly raise your legs up into the air until they are at a right angle with the floor.

4. Keep your knees straight; press down hard on the floor with your hands and swing your legs together over the back of your head. This will allow you to raise the lower part of your back from the floor. Now, leaving your elbows on the floor, support the lumbar region with your hands.

5. Slowly and carefully bring your legs up to the vertical position; don't strain. There's no need to hold your body rigid or tense in this position, be as relaxed as possible. Hold this position for five seconds.

6. Now bend your legs at the knees so that they come close down above your forehead. Hold this position for a few seconds.

7. To return your body to the floor; put both hands down and support yourself. Now slowly roll forwards and arch your neck so that you can keep the back of your head and your back on the floor.

8. When your lower back is resting on the floor, extend your legs straight out into the air and slowly lower them to the floor.

9. Let your body go completely limp and rest for at least a minute.

Important Points
- When you raise your legs from the floor keep them straight - this tones the tummy muscles.

- When you achieve each position, don't fidget.

- Close your eyes throughout the technique.

- As you move out of the posture, attempt to keep your movements graceful and controlled.

- Remember to arch your neck backwards so that your head remains on the floor as you roll forward to finish the routine.

Neck Movements

Benefits: strengthens the neck muscles; removes tension and stiff-ness from the neck.

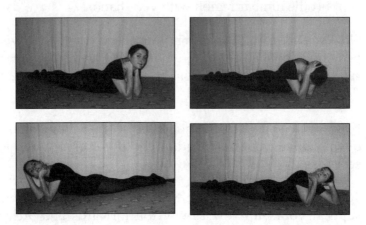

Technique:
1. When you have finished resting after the Cobra, prop yourself up on your elbows. Put your hands and fingers on the back of your head. Gently push your head down until your chin rests on the top of your chest. Hold this position for approximately twenty seconds.

2. Now slowly raise your head with hardly any movement of your hands, put your chin in the left palm and put your right hand securely on the back of your head. Slowly turn your head as far to the left as possible without straining. Hold this position for twenty seconds, remaining still throughout.

3. Slowly turn your head so that you can now rest your chin in your right palm and put your left hand securely on the back of your head. Slowly turn your head as far to the right as is possible without strain and hold this for twenty seconds, remaining still throughout.

4. Finally return your head to face forwards, lower your head till your forehead rests on the floor, and return your arms to your sides.

Important Points
- All neck movements must be made slowly and without strain.

- In the extreme positions, do not press too hard with the hands against the neck.

The Locust

Benefits: improves circulation; tones thighs and hips; strengthens the arms, abdomen, buttocks and legs; stimulates the endocrinal glands, liver, intestines, kidneys and reproductive organs.

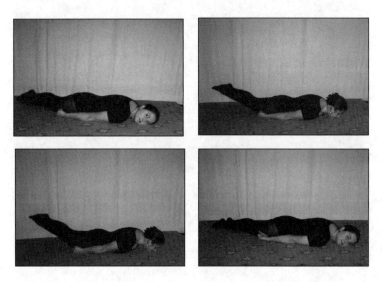

Technique:
1. Now that you have rested after the neck movements, you should be lying on your tummy with your cheek resting on the floor and your arms at your sides.

2. Turn your head and rest your chin on the floor (not your forehead as in the Cobra).

3. Make tight fists with both hands and put them, thumbs down, near your sides.

4. Inhale and half fill your lungs, holding the air in.

5. Push down hard with your fists and lift your legs as far from the floor as possible, keeping your knees as straight as possible. Hold this position for five seconds.

6. Slowly lower your legs back to the floor and exhale in a steady, controlled manner through your nose.

7. Rest your cheek on the floor.

Important Points
*   When you make fists with your thumbs on the floor, keep both arms close to your sides.

*   When you inhale, only half-fill your lungs; any more, and you could make the posture more difficult.

*   When you lift your legs, keep them both as straight as possible. If you find this exercise very difficult at first, you may slightly bend the your knees if it helps you to lift your legs.

*   At the end of the exercise lower your legs very slowly; don't just drop back to the floor.

*   Always breathe out through your nose.

Eye Exercise

Benefits: has a beneficial effect on the optic nerves and muscles; relieves eye-tension and fatigue; helps prevent eyestrain-related headaches.

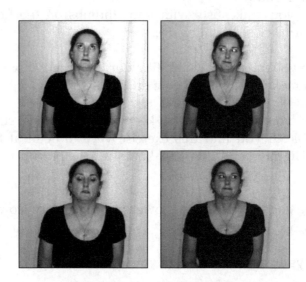

Technique:
When first doing this exercise, imagine facing a giant clock.

1. Look up as far as you can to twelve o'clock, really stretch the eyes and hold for a fraction of a second before moving on.

2. Now look as far over to the right to three o'clock.

3. Now down to six o'clock.

4. Up and over to the left for nine o'clock.

5. Back up to twelve o'clock.

6. In your own time, do another eight circuits in this way.

7. When you have completed all nine circuits, do a further nine circuits the opposite way around - twelve o'clock, then nine o'clock, then six o'clock, then three o'clock and back to twelve o'clock.

Important Points

*   Look as far into each position as you can and hold for about one second before moving to the next position.

*   Hold each position for a fraction of a second before moving on.

*   Complete nine rotations to the right and nine rotations to the left.

Forward Bend

Benefits: tones and conditions internal organs, and gives the spine a nice stretch.

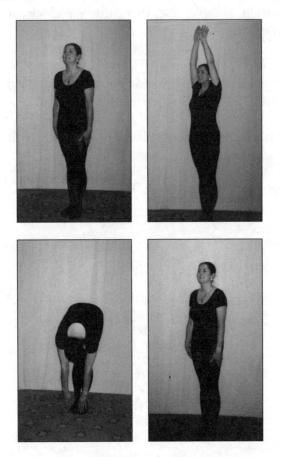

Technique:

1. Stand upright, facing forwards with your eyes closed. Put your hands and arms at your sides, with your feet close together. Breathe easily.

2. As you take a deep breath, lift your arms straight up in the air above your head; stretch your body to its full length.

3. Now pretending you have a hinge at your waist, bend and lower your trunk (whilst exhaling), bringing your hands to the floor if possible. Do not keep your knees locked too tightly - you may let them give a little if necessary.

4. Breathing easily, hold that position with your hands as close in to your feet as possible.

5. Breathing in gently, slowly return to a standing position, with your arms above your head.

6. Now exhale as you slowly lower your arms down to your sides again.

Important Points
• Do not strain.

• Carry out each movement in a rhythmic way.

Deep Peace Pose

Always finish your session of exercise with this posture.

Technique:

1. Lie down on your back.

2. Keep your hands and arms at your sides, palms facing upwards.

3. Let your whole body become loose and limp.

4. Close your eyes and just enjoy this peaceful position for three or more minutes.

Final Advice

This group of ten Yoga exercises and the Deep Peace Pose allow you to give your body a full stretch both internally and externally. Before doing the full sequence, I would suggest that you spend some time over a few days just practising each posture until you can do it without reading the instructions. Then decide on your programme. Some people do the sequence twice daily, others do them once a day. Certainly to gain any benefits they should be done on a regular basis at least once every other day.

You will notice that your body is always more supple in the evening than in the morning; because of this you might find the exercises easier to do in the evening. However, if you are only doing this programme once a day, I would suggest it be done in the morning.

Now a few short pieces of advice:

- Don't forget to breathe normally during this sequence.
- Let your exercises flow.
- Rest between each technique.
- Don't worry if at first you cannot reach too far into each position; you will still gain full benefits. Your body will adjust little by little over time.
- Exercises are best done before eating or at least three hours after a main meal.
- If you are doing the exercises when you first get up, try to have a bowel movement before doing them.
- It is also very beneficial to give your whole body a rub over with a flannel soaked in cold or luke-warm water, just prior to commencement of the sequence.

Summary

- Youthfulness is a very attractive state of being.
- Since earliest times and especially today, people search in vain everywhere for potions, or in fact anything that offers ways to stay young.
- We cannot stop growing older, but it is possible to slow down the effects of this process and remain strong and healthy throughout our lives.
- Within each of us lies a mighty life force; unfortunately, as most of us get older, we allow it to become dormant though lack of use.
- This force can be awakened. There are some simple Yoga stretching exercises, which can stimulate and awaken this force.
- These exercises were formulated several thousands of years ago. They are still useful today to help you gain health, comfort and happiness.
- When you have learned to do them they must by done frequently to experience and maintain good health and vitality.
- As time goes on, benefits are cumulative and you are likely to become more and more supple as the weeks and months go by.

Chapter Ten

Healing And Self-Healing

Lend thy soul's ear to every cry; Let not a tear the fierce sun dry;
Before thyself hath wiped away; Suffering Humanity's
pain, to stay.

Healing is taking place in all of us every moment of our lives. Our mind, through the immune system, is constantly balancing, purifying, and repairing our bodies. If this were not so we would not be here.

Illness And Stress

In Chapter One we discovered that overloads of stress were a significant contributing factor in many cases of illness. We also discovered that overloads of stress have many causative elements. These elements can be roughly classified as:

negative emotions, thoughts and attitudes
feelings of guilt
inner conflict
accidents
injury or illness transmitted from another person, creature, object or environment
selfishness and self-injury
hating self and others

Another contributive factor is said by some to be Karma - Fate and Destiny. This can offer explanations for apparent inequality and handicaps such as being born with deformity, illness or genetic defects and premature death. Certainly these conditions could be said to seem very unfair if we only have one chance at life.

God

Perhaps at this point I should define what I mean by the word `God', since I will be using it a few times in this chapter and later in the book.

God is something that is greater than ourselves, the Purpose or Creator of the universe and everything in it, including us. God is Divine Intelligence, Infinitely Powerful, the Potential of all Beauty, Perfection, Truth, Bliss and Energy. God is all that is real, all there is. God is the very centre of each and every one of us, Pure Consciousness. God is therefore all-knowing, all-seeing,; all-being, all-present everywhere, at every time. God is, of course completely beyond all human understanding. Tom Johanson (1986) states: "The spirit or deeper mind which healthily nourishes the soul is the thought of God".

The universe appears to have the ability to expand and move in an evolutionary way with laws and conditions. Mother Nature seems to be the womb of the universe through which these laws operate.

Our Unique Privilege

We are told that God has given mankind a gift that no other species on the planet has: that is, Free Will. Although we have instincts and desires like other species, we are able in many cases to choose whether to follow them or not. We therefore have the choice to ask and receive or to ignore. This ability to make choices is a very important factor in the healing work both for the healer and the recipient of the healing process. For example, the patient must desire to regain good health, whilst the healer must have the compassion to channel universal love, the healing energy.

Negative Conditions

All negative conditions could be explained as being out of balance or out of tune in some way with God or his representative Mother Nature. Often when we get lost in these out-of-balance states, we need help to regain our balance or equilibrium. At such times in our life, healing can literally be a Godsend.

Healing

Healing has been practised throughout the history of mankind. In Ancient Egypt, healing temples existed where people went for healing sleep and herbal treatments. The priests and priestesses in those days were the healers and they carried out elaborate rituals and purification ceremonies.

Primitive aboriginal peoples all over the world also have their individual witch doctors and medicine men and women who use incantations, herbal drugs, magic and spells in the healing work. Likewise in the ancient Christian Church healing was a very important part of ministry. After all, Jesus gave his apostles the authority to go out and heal. Today the Christian Church seems, at times, to neglect this command, or to no longer carry it out as much as it could.

Here, at the beginning of the Age of Aquarius, the West is beginning to awaken to the healing arts, which are mostly based on holistic approaches. In this chapter we will look at just a few types or styles of healing. These include spiritual, magnetic, psychic, and the use of crystals and colours.

Spiritual Healing

Spiritual healing occurs when, by the application of Spiritual Laws, the power of God manifests itself in a living being who is suffering from some disease, injury or malformation, and a change for the better takes place which is greater or faster than the normal medical belief system would expect. Often the sufferer is able to return to normal health and physical form. The healing might take place as a result of prayer by the sufferer or intercession by attunement with the Divine, by laying on of hands, or by other means.

Healers

A true healer may work in the presence of the sufferer - contact healing - or from a distance (sometimes thousands of miles away). This is referred to as non-contact or absent healing. A healer does not heal a sufferer, (s)he only channels divine cosmic energy. Most healers work intuitively in one of the following ways:

The healer puts hands first on the head and shoulders of the sick person, then on the part of the body requiring healing. The healer might pray to God at this time or simply be aware of divine energy flowing into and through the body, then from the healer's hands into the sick person.

The healer is aware of those parts of the sick person's body emitting abnormal energy patterns, indicating imbalances. The healer then places hands over these areas, directing the channelled healing power to that place.

The healer follows a pattern of placing the hands briefly on each part of the patient's body. This is usually initiated in the areas of the main chakras. Next the healer touches other parts of the patient's body. These will include joints in shoulders, arms, hands, fingers, thighs, knees, ankles, feet and toes. Some healers prefer to put their hands above or around the body of the patient without touching.

When laying on hands, the healer often puts one hand in front of the patient's body and one hand opposite at the other side at each place of contact. This allows the channelled healing energy to short circuit through the patient's body between the hands of the healer.

Some healers prefer the patient lying down, others sitting on a stool. There is no set position for the recipient/patient to sit or lie in. I personally ask my patient which position (s)he prefers. It doesn't really matter, as long as the patient is comfortable throughout the session.

Healing Procedures Used By Jesus

Throughout history there have been many great healers. Perhaps the most well-known and greatest was Jesus. Whether he was the Son of God or just a wonderful enlightened Master is beyond the scope of this book to consider. One thing we do know, however, is that Jesus was a spiritual healer. Jesus used a diversity of methods in his healing work. Here are just a few examples:

Luke 4:40-41. Type of healing: hands on.

"When the sun was setting, the people brought to Jesus all who had various kinds of sickness, and laying his hands on each one, he healed them. Moreover, demons came out of many people, shouting, "You are the Son of God!""

Mark 7:32-35. Type of healing: touch and prayer.

"There some people brought to him a man who was deaf and could hardly talk, and the begged him to place his hand on the man.

After he took him aside, away from the crowd. Jesus put his fingers into the man's ears. Then he spat and touched the man's tongue. He looked up to heaven and with a deep sigh said to him, "Ephphatha!" (which means, "Be opened!")"

Mark 8:22-26. Type of healing: intercession, faith of friends and contact by Jesus.

"They came to Bethsaida, and some people brought a blind man and begged Jesus to touch him. He took the blind man by the hand and led him outside the village. When he had spat on the man's and put his hands on him, Jesus asked, "Do you see anything?"

He looked up and said, "I see people; they look like trees walking around."

Once more Jesus put his hands on the man's eyes. Then his eyes were opened, his sight was restored, and he saw everything clearly."

Matthew 14: 36. Type of healing: faith and contact by the sick with the healer Jesus.

"People brought all their sick to him and begged him to let the sick just touch the edge of his cloak, and all who touched him were healed."

Matthew 9:2, 6-7. Type of healing: faith of friends, words alone from Jesus.

"Some men brought to him a paralytic, lying on a mat. When Jesus saw their faith, he said to the paralytic, "Take heart, son; your sins are forgiven."....

"But so that you may know that the Son of Man has authority on earth to forgive sins...." Then he said to the paralytic, "Get up, take your mat and go home." And the man got up and went home."

John 4:46-53. Type of healing: faith of the father and absent healing from Jesus.

"Once more he visited Cana in Galilee, where he had turned the water into wine. And there was a certain royal official whose son was sick at Capernaum. When this man heard that jesus had arrived in Galilee from Judea, he went to him and begged him to come and heal his son, who was close to death.

"Unless you people see miraculous signs and wonders," Jesus told him, "You will never believe."

The royal official said, "Sir, come down before my child dies."

Jesus replied, "You may go. Your son will love."

The man took jesus at his word and departed. While he was still on the way, his servants met him with the news that his boy was living. When he enquired as to the time when his son got better, they said to him, "The fever left him yesterday at the seventh hour.""

The Power Of Jesus
Throughout the Gospels there are many reports of Jesus' healing people. Perhaps the most interesting factor throughout is that Jesus never accepted the credit for the healing or miracles that he carried out. He always attributed everything to his Heavenly Father, God. Jesus also often went off to pray in private after a healing had taken place.

Magnetic Healing
Magnetic healing may be confused with spiritual healing, but it is not the same. In this type of healing the healer, through his ego, is using his own energy. This has the following limiting effects: the power is very limited, and it depletes the healer of personal energy and therefore the amount of healings he can participate in are limited. Using up personal energy can lower the healer's own levels of vibrancy and eventually lower his resistance to disease.

Most healers have some ego involvement during their work and often quite unwittingly use some of their own psychic energy. It is important therefore for the healer to sit down and relax for a few moments on completion of a healing, and focus on recovering and recharging energy levels, before carrying on with life.

Psychic Healing

Some people use the expression psychic healing to describe spiritual healing or channelling. They seem to be shy to admit to the existence of a Universal Loving Power or God. Technically `psyche' means `spirit' or `soul'. Other people use the word to mean using their own psychically-developed powers or invoking unknown entities or forces. This can be a dangerous practice, one I would not recommend.

Holistic Healing

All effective healing should be holistic. This means treating the whole person or being. It includes mind, body, spirit and emotions. Each of us is a reflection of our universe. In the Bible (Genesis 1:26-28), it clearly states that each of us is made in the image of God. Each of us contains elements of male and female, positive and negative. What we think and what we imagine make us what we are. So let your mind be filled with healthful thoughts; gently guide your mind forward with a realisation that you are a child of God made in his image out of all the elements from which the universe was created. You are here now because you are known and loved by the centre of creation, Love itself. Relax and flow, feel peace and balance within you.

A Healing Exercise

1. Get yourself into a comfortable position. You may lie down or sit, whichever you prefer.

2. Breathe comfortably and allow your whole body to relax. You may use *The Calm Routine* or *The Balancing Breath* whilst doing this.

3. Now imagine going back through time until you find yourself in a particular place at some time, being in the presence of your chosen healer. It might be Jesus, The Blessed Lady or a favourite saint; it could be Buddha or another advanced soul.

4. Now be aware of feelings of love and compassion that are surrounding the healer.

5. Look into the eyes of the healer and ask silently for healing. Realise that no great being would refuse to give this to you.

6. Now be aware of the loving, healing energy flowing from that Divine Being into your body, filling you with soothing, healing sensations.

7. Soon you will be aware of changes taking place in areas of your body - perhaps tingling or changes of temperature.

8. Stay with this for some time and reflect on things in your life that you might now decide to do differently.

9. After a while - it might be several minutes - you can decide to take some slightly deeper breaths before opening your eyes and returning into the here and now.

10. Any thoughts or ideas about changes you want to make can now be noted.

11. Later you might formulate these ideas into affirmations to assist with the changes.

Crystals And Their Healing Qualities

Next we will take a peep into the wonderful, healing world of crystals. Crystals can be used to help focus our mental energy for healing. They are said to give off beneficial vibrations.

Clear Quartz Crystals

These attractive crystals have the ability to amplify and transmit subtle vibrations. They are a symbol of elemental wholeness. They are formed from the four great elemental powers of creation: earth, from which they are born; water, contained within their structure; fire, their electrical quality; and air, the quality of allowing light to flow freely.

Technology And Quartz

In our high tech society we employ quartz in many ways:

In oscillators, for vibration at very precise frequencies.

In capacitors, to modify energy.

In many types of equipment for transmission, control and storage of energy.

In ionizers, to absorb positive and emit negative ions.

Quartz In Healing
Healers who use crystals in their work consider them to be an all-purpose tool for rebalancing human energy at all levels of consciousness. Quartz crystals can assist in amplifying, focusing, directing and bringing integration to a person's entire being. They are said to reflect, and then project, the white, healing light within them. This strengthens the aura, giving extra protection against negative energies and debilitating effects of electrical currents from TV sets, microwaves, or other sources of uncontrolled electromagnetic fields. Clear quartz can be programmed to fulfil a healing role for many different types of illness and disorders.

Crystal Types
Crystals come in many natural shapes and with special individual qualities. Here are a few:

Generator Crystals are usually clear, sometimes with a cloudy base. Size and dimension does not necessarily indicate the degree of power projected by each individual crystal. Generators can be of any type and colour of quartz or mineral and may contain inclusions, rainbows or phantoms within their structure.

Rainbows are said to protect us from any evil we may meet. Inclusions are made of petrified water and fill the interior of the crystal with a display of rainbow colours or silver shapes.

Phantoms are supposed to be the ghosts of lives past, milestones throughout the development and growth of the host crystal. Crystals containing phantoms are said to have a calming effect if held in the hand whilst relaxing or meditating.

Double Terminal Crystals. During their evolution, these types of crystals have developed points at both ends. They are used to recirculate energy, and to absorb and transmute negative energies, whilst re-energising and harmonising the chakras. They are said to be used by those communicating through telepathy, although I have as yet no evidence of this in my work.

Tabular Crystals are extremely vibrant, flat quartz. They are comparatively rare. They are said to be powerful, and are used for bridging and balancing energies within relationships between two people, places, chakras or elements.

Clusters are groups of single crystals sharing one base. They harmonise with each other and reflect a powerful group energy. I use an amethyst cluster to purify my quartz crystal after a healing session. I just lie the crystal on top of the cluster for a couple of hours, and it renews its energy.

Wands are long single crystals and can be used for pointing at out of balance areas of sickness, to project the healing light. They can also be held in the hand or placed on a nearby table during periods of meditation or learning.

Other Crystals

Gemstones of different types and colours are reputed to have specialised qualities:

Agate: multi-coloured swirls. Calms the nerves, helps to increase confidence and self-esteem. Is said to bring good fortune to its owner.

Aquamarine: colour - blue. Quickens the intellect and opens one up to greater self-knowledge. It contributes to spiritual vision.

Amber: colour - transparent orange. Used for making and breaking spells. It is calming and promotes self-healing.

Amethyst: purple-coloured quartz. This is used to calm the mind; it has a balancing effect and helps increase awareness. It is known to ease head pain and encourage relaxation. Put an amethyst under your pillow for sounder sleep. It helps to purify the blood and traditionally was believed to protect against intoxication.

Aventurine: usually green with inclusions of mica. It is good for equalising blood pressure, and creates calmness and serenity. It is good for treating skin disease. It is said to bring good fortune and luck in love and sport.

Bloodstone: this stone has red and green combinations. It helps to purify the blood and detoxify the organs.

Calcite: colour - white or grey but can also be found in shades of yellow, green, red, purple, blue, brown or black. This soothes away anxiety, expands awareness and aids intuition.

Carnelian: is usually coloured orange. It has an elevating effect, and is good for grounding, focusing and concentration.

Citrine: this crystal is a deep yellow. It is said to activate the power of thought. It helps to equalise emotions and in building self-confidence. It is also said to help in diabetes.

Emerald: colour - green. This is said to give insight into the future and acts as an emotional stabiliser, and is good for tired eyes.

Fluorite: colour - green. Used for grounding, balancing and focusing energies. It absorbs and transmutes negativity, and is used for opening the chakras. It is also used for mental and physical healing, and is especially useful in strengthening bone tissue.

Garnet: colour - red. Used to attract love, protect the owner from infection, and increase determination.

Jade: colour - deep green. It is said to promote longevity. It is used for treating kidney and bladder complaints.

Jasper: colour - red. It is said to offer protection from witchcraft, and have a soothing effect on the nerves.

Jet: colour - black. It aids grieving, quietens fears.

Lapis Lazuli: colour - usually blue with flecks of purple, red and white. Lifts depression and promotes self-confidence. It is the friendship stone and helps with introspection.

Malachite: colour - green. It raises the spirits and increases hope, health and happiness, and attracts physical and material benefits.

Moonstone: colour - pale yellow. It attracts happiness, is calming and encourages love.

Obsidian: found in several colours. A revealer of inner hidden truths, it is also used for divination.

Opal: found in a variety of colours. This is soothing, helps in controlling bad tempers and promotes calmness. It is said to increase psychic abilities, and believed to be good for the lungs.

Peridot: colour - green. Used by those developing inner vision, it is called the stone of the seer. It opens the mind and prevents negativity.

Rose Quartz: this is a pleasant pink colour due to its manganese content. It is soothing to the heart and is helpful in healing wounds and skin disorders. It gives feelings of inner peace and gives off lovely, gentle vibrations. It makes a person receptive to beauty.

Ruby: colour - red. It alleviates worries, and improves confidence, wisdom, energy and courage.

Sapphire: colour - transparent blue. It strengthens faith, has a calming effect on the nerves, and attracts good energy.

Selenite: colour - transparent and colourless. It is a form of gypsum. The main function of this crystal is to help expand mental powers.

Smoky Quartz: this is black or brown in colour due to its content of carbon, iron or titanium. It can stimulate and purify the energy centres. It has a stabilising influence and helps lift depression. It is useful in healing, especially in the lower and abdominal areas of the body. Cooking clear quartz in a hot oven makes so-called smoky quartz, but this does not have the same qualities as genuine smoky quartz.

Sodalite: colour - blue. It aids sleep, and helps to lower high blood pressure and balance the metabolism.

Tiger-eye: colour - usually orange and black stripes. It attracts good luck and aids the insight into oneself. It also offers protection from psychic attack.

Topaz: colour - usually yellow. This is used to strengthen blood vessels, improve thought processes, and calm mind and body.

Tourmaline: colour - black. This is an all-round useful crystal used to balance and promote confidence, cheerfulness and inspiration.

Turquoise: colour - blue. It shields from harmful influences, and attracts friendship.

Choosing A Crystal

Crystals can be purchased from psychic fairs, new-age shops and from crystal wholesalers. When buying a crystal, take your time and look carefully at the full display of crystals. If possible, pick up each crystal that you are attracted to. Those that know a lot about crystals say that you do not choose the crystal, but rather it chooses you, by attraction.

Intuition plays a major part in how you choose to use the colours. Whatever of the above methods feels right, must be right for you, and you will surely benefit from its application.

Cleansing Your Crystal

Never use a crystal until you have cleansed it. This can be accomplished in one of the following ways:

- By soaking in sea-salt water overnight. Use one teaspoonful of sea salt per pint of warm water. When the water clears, submerge the crystal in it overnight, preferably in moonlight. In the morning, rinse in fresh water before use.
- By soaking it in sea-salt water during the daytime, and, if possible, in a sunny place. Then rinse in clean water before use.
- By burying it in the garden for a day or two, then washing it under a cold tap or, better still, in a stream of running water.
- By resting the crystal on a cluster of amethyst, usually for a period of two hours or more. Then rinse it in fresh water before use.

Programming Or Energising Your Crystal

Immediately after cleansing the crystal is the ideal time to programme it for its particular use.

1. Stand holding the crystal in line with your heart, preferably in sunlight, or, if female energy is needed do this, in moonlight (full moon if possible). Soon you will feel tingling, usually in your fingers.

2. Now hold the crystal in line with your brow at about arm's length and look into it.

3. Silently think about the purpose and type of healing the crystal is to be used for. You will usually feel another tingling sensation in your hand, coming from the crystal. This indicates that it is now energised. The crystal will hold this programme. Always cleanse the crystal after use.

Changing A Programme Or Re-energising

This is accomplished by carrying out a purification and then going through the programming procedure again, this time thinking about the new use you require the crystal for.

Using Crystals For Self-Healing

Carrying a crystal around with you in your pocket or purse or wearing it in some way will often help with self-healing. Always choose a crystal suitable for the particular healing. Ensure that it is purified and programmed for your specific needs. Occasionally you may put it in your hand and gently hold it over the area requiring healing for a short time, whilst staying in a relaxed state. Never forget to purify your crystal frequently, especially after healing use.

Energising Water With Crystals

Your crystal can be used to energise drinking water to assist in the healing process. A simple example might be: you are an excitable person and wish to have a calmer attitude. You consult your list and find that aventurine is a green crystal that is said to promote calmness and relaxation.

1. First purify your aventurine crystal. Then energise it.

2. Now pour out a generous quantity of pure, filtered water into a glass, pot or china container. (Avoid metal containers.)

3. Put your aventurine crystal in the water and leave either in sunlight or moonlight overnight.

4. Whenever you require a drink of water pour some from the container into your glass. As you drink the water be aware of the soothing influence it invites within you. This water may also be used for washing or bathing yourself or others in.

Note: any of the crystals can be used in this way to treat a relevant condition.

Clear Quartz is the most pure crystal. It can be energised or programmed to treat any condition or illness. Simply after purification follow the instructions for programming/energising, and as you hold the Quartz at brow level, think into it the purpose you require it for and, if you can remember, the colour of the particular crystal that would normally fulfil that role.

Chakra Balancing

Crystals can also be used for balancing the chakral energies. Here is a list of the crystals that may be used for each chakra:

Root or Base Chakra - Red
Garnet, bloodstone, ruby, red jasper, black tourmaline, obsidian, smoky quartz.

Sacral/Spleen Chakra - Orange
Carnelian, amber, peach, citrine, gold topaz, gold calcite.

Solar Plexus Chakra - Yellow
Amber, tiger-eye, gold calcite, gold topaz, gold.

Heart Chakra - Green (also rose)
Aventurine, rose quartz, ruby, emerald, malachite, green jade.

Throat Chakra - Blue
Blue topaz, sodalite, aquamarine, turquoise.

Brow/Third Eye Chakra - Indigo
Quartz crystal, sapphire, tourmaline, lapis lazuli, sodalite.

Crown Chakra - Brilliant Violet
Amethyst, diamond, purple fluorite, selenite, quartz crystal.

Simple Chakra-Balancing Exercise Using Crystals

1. Purify and energise one crystal from each chakra grouping.

2. Lie down comfortably and just let go of all tension in your body, breathing easily.

3. You can have some gentle background music playing if you wish.

4. Place the appropriate crystal on the part of your body corresponding to its chakra. (Except for the Crown Chakra - that crystal can be placed on the floor immediately above and close to your head.)

5. Now relaxing and without strain, put your mind on the Crown Chakra and imagine the crystal glowing and feel the gentle energy flow into your crown. Stay with it just for a few moments, then move on to the brow and repeat the process.

6. Continue down through the chakras in this way, visualising each crystal glowing in its particular colour, energising its centre, until you reach the Base Chakra.

7. When you have completed this circuit just lie there for a few more minutes, allowing the energies to come into balance. If you feel any discomfort in some part of your body, place your hand or hands gently over that area and, if necessary, massage it until you feel more comfortable.

8. Be aware of any emotions or thoughts that arise during this time and make a mental note of them.

9. You may lie here and daydream for a while or have a nap before finishing the session. Afterwards purify these crystals before further use.

There are many ways to use crystals in healing. Some people put the appropriate crystal under their pillow to encourage more satisfying sleep patterns. Clear quartz crystals can be positioned in the four corners of a room pointing towards the centre to create a purifying energy zone/environment for relaxation and recreational activities; rose quartz and clear crystals can be put near plants to encourage healthy growth. For those of you who wish to gain more information about the vast and wonderful world of crystals, see *Crystal Healing* by Edmund Harold as listed in the Bibliography at the back of this book.

Colour Healing

Light is known to have a positive effect on all living things. The whole planet - the oceans, the earth, everything we see manifested as mineral, plant, animal and human - is dependent upon light and its amazing properties and radiations for its existence. Not only the physical world but also the higher worlds - of which the universe is a manifestation, an outward sign - the etheric, astral, mental and spiritual planes all depend upon the same source, namely light. Each, of course, has its own spectrum of vibration. Remember, there are unlimited vibratory levels outside the human range and scope. Even some of the animals are aware of broader spheres of vibration than us. For example:

- The sense of smell in dogs is hundreds of times more efficient than in humans.
- The sight of birds of prey is so acute that an eagle is able to see a mouse from thousands of feet away.
- Bats send out sound signals which inform them of obstructions many feet ahead of them.
- Sharks can detect prey in the water from miles away.

Cosmic Rays

The true Cosmic Rays are spiritual forces emanating from the Divine White Light. The Rays are perpetually vibrating, not only on the surface of the earth, but also above and through it, encircling the globe in streams of endless, inexhaustible energy. S. G. J. Ouseley (1949) says, "The seven major colour rays fill space and permeate the soul and being. They are the manifestation of the seven great cosmic periods. They correspond to the seven major glandular centres in the human body. In the Spirit of the Rays exist all the potentialities of the higher beings". In the Ageless Wisdom it is believed that, `As above so below, as within so without, as in the macrocosm so also in the microcosm'. Mary Anderson (1979) explains, "Colour expresses the way we think and then reacts back on us from our surroundings, either raising or lowering our spirits". The same rays and forces surround and permeate every part of us on every level. As I said earlier, if there are any obstructions in a psyche the flow, in this case of light energy, will become obstructed and pain, and illness are usually the result.

The Seven Rays
Rose-Red Ray: has a direct effect on the Base Chakra. Used for treating blood-deficiency diseases, anaemia, low energy levels, etc..

WARNING: The Red Ray should be used with caution. Avoid using it if you suffer from high blood pressure, stroke, thrombosis, irritability, bad temper, etc. In these sorts of conditions, use very pale pink for a very short period of time.

Orange Ray: effects the Sacral Chakra. It is warm, positive and stimulating. It influences the process of digestion, stimulates and works on the spleen, is used for treating nervous and mental debility, for relief of asthma, regulating phlegm. It can be used in drinking water whilst bathing in blue light for treatment of epilepsy.

Yellow Ray: works on the Solar Plexus Chakra. It is magnetic, has a tonic effect on the nerves, influences higher thinking processes, is inspiring and stimulating, cleanses and purifies the whole system. It is useful in treating dyspepsia, flatulence, diabetes, and constipation.

Green Ray: controls the Heart Chakra. It is a vibration for harmony and balance, and is fundamentally important to the nervous system. Said to be nature's master tonic, it is soothing and sympathetic; it strongly influences the control and distribution of the blood supply. It restores tired nerves, gives new energy, is good for treating heart conditions and for relief from neuralgic-type headaches.

166

WARNING: In cases of low blood pressure use dark green; in cases of high blood pressure use pale green light.

Blue Ray: controls the Throat Chakra and is antiseptic and astringent. It is useful for treating insomnia, helps reduce inflammation and fever, eases sore throats, hoarseness, goitre, fevers, palpitation, colic, jaundice, skin abrasions, cuts, burns, etc., and eases rheumatic conditions.

Indigo Ray: influences the Brow Chakra, central part of the head and pineal gland. It has dominion over eyes, ears and nose. It is used for preliminary cataract treatment, inflammation of the eyes, deafness, pneumonia, and is effective in the treatments of nervous and mental disorders,lung diseases, pneumonia, asthma, bronchitis, consumption, and dyspepsia. It is said to expel negative elements in consciousness and relieve mental disorders.

Violet Ray: stimulates the Crown Chakra and controls the pituitary gland. It is the highest elemental ray in human make-up and it governs the brain, mental and spiritual nature. It is suitable for treating nervous conditions, insomnia, mental disorders, cataract and other optical distortions.

The basis of treatment, whether physical or super-physical, is the restoring and recharging of the body cells with the correct colour vibration through the glandular centres or chakras.

The most common ways that colour healers use remedial rays are:
1. By reflecting coloured light from a lamp onto an area or the whole body of the subject.
2. For suggesting colours into various areas of the body with words during relaxation.
3. In teaching the subject various breathing exercises combined with visualisation and affirmation.
4. For charging drinking and bathing water with healing vibrations.
5. Using a variety of foods for their colours' healing benefits, as well as their nutritional values.
6. To advise people on which personal healthful colours to include in their clothing and home decor.

Using Coloured Lights

From your electrical supplier get the following coloured bulbs: rose-red, orange, yellow, light green, dark green, blue, indigo, and violet or purple. Then get a piece of board or plank about four feet long. Next get a handyman to do the following:

1. Affix onto the board about every six inches eight electric light sockets.
2. Wire the sockets to a simple breaker switch so that you can sit about six feet from the lights and change from one colour to another. Although not vital, a dimmer switch would be useful as well.
3. Now put the bulbs into the sockets in the following order from left to right: rose-red, orange, yellow, light green, dark green, blue, indigo, violet/purple.
4. Whenever you wish to use lights, you can sit in a dark room and switch on whichever colour(s) you are using at that time.

Note: Until you have this device you could use a table lamp and put the appropriate coloured bulb in it. The disadvantage of this method is that you can only use one colour at a time and then you will have to change the bulb.

A Scenario Using Colour Healing

You are a student shortly to take exams. You need to revise but find that you are feeling anxious, unable to concentrate and also unable to sleep well at night. You frequently get sweaty and hot when thinking about the forthcoming tasks, and feel that you are not going to be able to pass your exams. Symptoms are therefore: anxiety, resultant insomnia, lack of concentration, low self-esteem and lack of confidence.

1. Checking through the list of rays you discover that yellow ray has a tonic effect on nerves and is inspiring and stimulating. The green ray produces harmony and balance, is soothing, restores tired nerves and gives new energy. The violet ray governs the brain and mental faculties, treats nervous conditions and can be used to dispel insomnia.
2. You then check through the systems of treatment list and discover you have several methods of application. You decide to carry out the following treatment.

3. Sit down in a quiet place. Get relaxed using *The Calm Routine*.
4. Now decide that you will reflect upon your chosen colours - in this case, yellow, green and violet.
5. Imagine in your mind's eye each colour, one after the other, filling your whole body. Enjoy this experience. Or you could use the light device, switching on yellow, green and violet lights one after the other as you relax and bathe in each ray for a few moments. Use your intuitive judgement on how long those moments are.

Energising Water With Colour

Drinking or bathing water may be energised with an appropriate colour as follows:

Fill a container with fresh water. Switch on the appropriate coloured light and/or sitting comfortably, hold your hands above the water and gently visualise the colour whilst thinking of the particular condition you require the water to treat. Spend about five or more minutes in this practice. Although the water now still retains its normal contextual value, it is energised and can be drunk whenever you require a drink or bathed in or used to apply over a diseased or poorly energised area. This water can also be beneficially used in animal healing, and for watering plants.

Summary

- Healing is taking place in each of us at this moment.
- Stress overload may interfere with the healing process and cause illness. Other causative factors in disease may include Karma, Fate and Destiny.
- God is the absolute creative force in the universe.
- Mother Nature is the name for the laws of the universe.
- As humans we have been given a unique gift: Free Will.
- All negative conditions could be said to be signs of being out of tune with God or Mother Nature. Many negative conditions can be a result of misuse of free will.
- Healing has been practised throughout all time. All the ancient cultures have examples of every type of healing.
- Healers are usually compassionate people who wish to see others well and healthy.
- There are many types of healing.
- Spiritual healing occurs when the universal energy is channelled into the body of a sick person, usually by the power of prayer, intercession, or hands-on application from a healer. The person usually makes a faster than usual recovery.
- There is no set way of carrying out spiritual healing.
- Jesus is perhaps one of the most well-known Spiritual Healers through time.
- Jesus used many types of spiritual healing: laying on of hands, prayer, words, intercession by friends of the sick, people's faith in him, and absent healing.
- Jesus never took any personal credit for the healings; he always thanked the Father God in Heaven.
- Magnetic healing is very limited. The healer is using his own personal magnetism and therefore, besides depleting his own reserves, limits the work that can be accomplished.
- Psychic healing may or may not be spiritual healing. Sometimes it is the person using his/her own energy or psychic magic, or invoking unknown powers to do the work. This is not to be recommended.
- Holistic healing. All healing should be holistic. This means treating the whole person as a complete being.
- Crystals can be used in the healing work.

- Crystals are said to reflect universal light and can be used to channel it into those who are ill.
- Clear quartz is perhaps the most versatile type of crystal. It is used in many processes with high tech equipment. It can also be programmed for any type of healing.
- There are many other types, shapes and colours of crystals used in healing. Each has its own colour vibrations and each is useful for treating certain conditions.
- Crystals are classified in the following ways: generator crystals, double terminals, tabulars, clusters, wands.
- Types of crystals vary in colour depending on their mineral contents. There are many shades and colours of crystals conforming to the colours of the rainbow and the Chakras.
- Crystals can be used for healing self and others, energising, concentration, communication, balancing, purifying and many other purposes.
- Care must be taken when choosing crystals. It is said that the crystal chooses the owner by attraction.
- Crystals must be cleansed before and after use.
- Crystals can also be energised and/or programmed. Programmes can be changed or modified.
- Clear quartz can be programmed to take the place of any other crystal for healing purposes.
- Colour healing is carried out by using the seven Cosmic Rays. (Some healers use more than seven colours.)
- Colour healing may be produced through visualisation techniques, coloured lamps, food, clothing, looking at nature, charging water etc..
- Intuition plays a very great part in this form of healing.

Chapter Eleven

Meditation

When we return to Godhead, to live in unity;
We keep our earned uniqueness, for all Eternity.

Many people who come to me for therapy are unhappy, stressed and, above all, not quite sure what life is all about. Whether they know it or not, those who are in middle life and still suffering are mostly searching for identity and are somewhat confused. The questions they seem to be asking themselves are: Who am I? Why am I here? What is the purpose of my life? Why do I suffer? These are questions that many great people have asked themselves throughout the history of the human race. Buddha was one of them. For people who are experiencing these phenomena, I often recommend or teach one of several types of meditational practices.

Erica Smith and Nicholas Wilks (1988) claim that deciding which technique to use can be difficult. They go on to say,

> *"...techniques are not ends in themselves, but means to achieving a state that lies beyond technique."*

Naomi Humphreys (1987) states:

> *"Meditation is not confined to the young and unorthodox at heart. ...The young and the not so young, housewives, businessmen, professionals and the unwaged, these all share the experience of meditation."*

Most meditation begins with focusing upon an object or thing. This may be anything from breathing to an apple, memory, colour, sound, deity, saint, quality, etc. Eventually, through this concentration upon one object, the incessant chatter of thoughts will slow down. The meditator can then develop an ability to stand aside and be aware that the thoughts themselves are only ripples upon the mind-stuff. As the thoughts quieten, the meditator will eventually pass beyond the thinking process altogether. This process of concentration, meditation and contemplation is an underlying principle of all meditative practices.

When one reaches the final contemplative state, therein lies peace and freedom from all attachment and pain, and one enters the absolute silence.

Content Of Meditation

Meditation can be said to be subjective or objective, stilling or flowing. Within any period of meditation you can experience some, any or all of these conditions. These often occur spontaneously and cannot be contrived. Thus, whether we are using subjective or objective, stilling or flowing types of meditation we are in fact focusing upon one thing. The mind and its contents are one and the same. Later, I will describe different types of meditation techniques. From these you may choose one that you feel comfortable with. Here are a few tips that I have found very useful in helping me to benefit from this practice:

- Choose a place for meditation where you are unlikely to be disturbed.
- Practise regularly once or twice daily.
- Make sure the room temperature is just right for you, as your body temperature is likely to fall during the practice.
- Get really comfortable sitting, not lying down.
- Perhaps do *The Calm Routine* for a minute prior to commencement.
- Do not meditate within two hours after a main meal. You may meditate right up to before a meal.
- Do not take any alcohol or non-prescribed drugs before meditating.
- If you feel uncomfortable and want to adjust your position, feel free to do so. An uncomfortable person cannot meditate.
- Do not have music playing in the room or ticking clocks.
- If you wish to time yourself, use a wristwatch. Consult it before starting. When you think it's time to finish, bring your watch up close to your face and just squint at it. Never suddenly open the eyes wide at the end of your practice.

- Always lie down for a few minutes after a meditation and before getting up and returning life. This allows your metabolic rate to get back to normal.
- Don't worry if you fall asleep. New mediators often fall asleep during the first few meditations, but remember that when you fall asleep you are not meditating. Eventually you will be able to meditate without falling asleep. That's great.

CAUTION: all meditative techniques cause internal adjustments and release of trapped stress overload. It is therefore important to do the following:
- Whatever kind of meditation you choose to do for the first couple of weeks, keep to a small sessional time, say ten minutes twice daily. Then when you have accustomed yourself to the practice, increase the time each week up to a maximum of twenty minutes' actual meditation per session. Never exceed twenty minutes unless under the supervision of a qualified teacher of meditation.
- Whenever you are going through a rough patch in life, shorten your meditation time until things get better, and then gradually return to your original timing. Always take a few minutes' rest after meditating before going back to your life.
- It is also very important that you get regular daily exercise perhaps a twenty-minute walk daily. All meditators require regular exercise.

Stilling Meditation
1. Sit comfortably with your eyes closed.
2. Place all of your attention on your breathing; remain still, watchful.
3. Be aware of the coming and the going of the in-breath, the out-breath, and those turning moments between the breaths.
4. After a few minutes you will be aware of an incredible stillness.
5. Then move your focus, easily, gently, slowly on all parts of the body.
6. First, be aware of the sensations in your head, face and neck, then down the shoulders, the arms and the hands, then down the body into the thighs, legs and feet.

7   Now return your attention back to your breathing.

8.   Spend some time going through this awareness process several times for a few minutes.

Only do a few minutes twice a day for the first couple of weeks and then increase the practice until you are able to do about fifteen to twenty minutes twice a day. Always remember to spend a few minutes lying down with your eyes open before getting back into life after this practice.

Flowing Meditation
In this type of meditation we will work with a sequence rather than a single point of focus. One popular practice is called `inner voice meditation'.

Inner Voice Meditation
This technique involves the same qualities of direction and concentration as any other type of meditational practice. The important difference is that it is based upon focusing on a specific idea such as a symbol like the cross, or a star or a phrase such as `God is love' or `Allah is just'.

Technique:
1.   Follow all the tips given at the beginning of this chapter.

2.   Now choose your symbol or phrase.

3.   Spend some time just being aware of this focus.

4.   Associated ideas might appear in your mind, gently observe them as they pass through.

5.   Always remember to be aware of coming back to your focal idea.

6.   Continue this practice for some moments.

7.   Now, gently let go of your focus and lie down with eyes open, resting for a while.

8.   Finally make any notes on your insights.

You may continue doing this practice once or twice a day using the same symbol or phrase for days, weeks or months until you feel that you have gained as much insight as you can from your meditation.

For those who wish to develop compassion, here is a simple yet beautiful form of meditation.

1. Get comfortable as for other techniques.

2. Think first of the suffering of people in your family or close friends.

3. Next, consider how wonderful it would be if these people could feel peace and relief from their suffering.

4. Feel the desire to set them free from this suffering.

5. Send out love and light to them; imagine seeing them free from the kind of pain that you know they have.

6. Next, send out thoughts for people outside your immediate circle and send love, light and compassion, perhaps a silent prayer to your chosen deity.

7. Finally consider all suffering beings, animals and our planet, and send out healing light and love.

8. Now just allow yourself to let go of these thoughts and return back to your conscious, awake state. As with other techniques, take some time to lie down with your eyes open before getting up and returning back into your everyday life.

Visualisation In Relaxing Meditation

Earlier in the book we learned about visualisation for goal setting. Here we will use it to create states for improving our general health whilst enhancing our ability to see into the inner world. There is no doubt that inner vision is an enormously powerful tool for growth and development. It can give both psychological and physical benefits and it is now used effectively in therapies and treatments for disease and illness. It plays a great role in some forms of alternative cancer treatments.

Visualisation Meditation

This form of meditation contains elements of objectiveness and flowingness.

1. Get comfortable. You may lie down or sit for this type of meditation.

2. Close your eyes and be aware of your breathing.

3. After a minute or two, when you are relaxed, imagine lying or sitting in a place that is for you wonderful. It might be in the countryside, a garden, a forest, or near a lake, ocean or river.

4. Feel yourself sitting or lying comfortably in this place, seeing the sights in the shapes and colours that most please you.

5. You might notice the blue sky like infinity above you.

6. Listen to the sounds and take in any pleasant aromas that you associate with this place.

7. You may, at first, see yourself in this place, then float into yourself so that you are looking out from your eyes onto this blissful scene. Find yourself sitting or lying comfortably, enjoying this experience.

8. Spend a few moments allowing yourself just to luxuriate in these sensations of pleasure.

9. Now on each out-breath repeat, `I am floating into bliss'; feel your body becoming lighter and lighter. Now feel yourself flowing into the blue sky outwards and onwards, beyond time and space into a state of bliss-filled calmness. Enjoy this state for some time.

10. When you feel ready to return, be aware of yourself gradually entering your body in the place in your vision where you are lying or sitting.

11. Finally tell yourself to open your eyes.

12. Don't get up straight away. Just lie here for a few minutes to allow your metabolism to return to normal.

Objective Meditation

This type of meditation encompasses many different techniques, some of them are very advanced. Advanced techniques include the use of a Koan and Form and Formless Contemplations. These types of meditation are beyond the scope of this book.

Objective meditations recognise a Spiritual Power. This power might be a personal power, perhaps God, a Deity, a Master or holy person. Mantra meditation can also be counted as an objective practice.

Simple Meditation

1. Choose a picture of your chosen object or holy person.

2. Sit down and carry out the usual preparation.

3. Place the picture in front of you at eye-level. Gaze steadily at it; blink only when essential.

4. Take in every detail.

5. When you feel you have the picture fixed in your mind's eye, close your eyes as if taking a photograph.

6. When the image begins to fade, open your eyes and gaze at the picture once more.

7. Be careful not to scan the picture with your eyes.

8. Take in the whole picture at first and then study and focus on one area at a time until you have it clearly in your mind.

9. Take in the meaning that this picture conveys to you.

10. It might encompass love, compassion and peacefulness. Check through the picture to identify how this is represented.

11. If it is a picture of your favourite saint, look deeply into the eyes and feel the qualities that these reflect for you.

12. Soon the picture will seem to come to life for you.

13. After doing this for some time you might decide to make an audiotape of your description of the qualities the picture portrays for you. You might later play this tape when you do your future meditations on this object/person.

14. Always take some time at the end of each meditation to return to a normal state before getting up and returning into life.

Mantra Meditation

This type of meditation may take on many forms. Mantras may be conceptual or non-conceptual sounds. They can be used in concentrative or non-concentrative techniques. **Conceptual sounds** convey a conscious meaning to the user. Examples of conceptual mantra meditations could be the Roman Catholic Rosary, or chanting Latin litanies. **Non-conceptual sounds** can be mantras given by a Guru to a disciple. Mantras are empowered sounds that have qualities within their vibrations. One of the best known forms of meditation using non-conceptual sounds is transcendental meditation. **Transcendental meditation** has helped millions of people to relax and gain better qualities of life. I teach a very simple non-concentrative mantra meditation technique which I call **Dynamic Deep Meditation**. Unfortunately it cannot be taught from a book. I teach it to my students and clients at my practice.

Prayer

Meditation and contemplation could be classified as types of silent inner prayer. Prayer can take many forms. Most people that I know seem to think that prayer is old fashioned and doesn't work. No wonder it doesn't work for them: most people who decry prayer have either never tried it or are praying for the wrong thing. However, watch these same sceptics if one of their children is hurt or someone is dying. You will hear them saying `Dear God, please help me', or `please don't let mum die'. Later when the crisis is over God seems to be totally forgotten, and appreciation is rarely given.

My mum, God rest her soul, knew how to pray. She believed in the Sacred Heart of Jesus. I'm sure she thought Jesus walked around with a big red heart hanging out of his garment. This didn't matter; mum had a simple devoted belief that if anyone was in trouble, she would pray to the Sacred Heart for them and that he would help them. Guess what, many of her prayers were answered. I have benefited from my mum's absolute faith in her Lord. I have had many tragedies in my life but whenever mum has prayed for me something strange and wonderful has always happened. Mum was a lovely person and she always told me, `Never forget to thank the Lord for his mercy'. Yes, she always thanked her Lord, even before the prayer was answered; she expected it and knew it would happen, and usually it did.

Prayer, for me, is something that is always happening. You don't have to kneel down and you don't have to pray out loud, but praying opens up the soul to higher states and permits wonders to occur.

Simple Prayer
Do the following for one week each morning when you wake, and see the differences that occur in you and your life:

1. When you wake, thank your Deity, Master or higher self for another day of life.

2. Ask for guidance during your day.

3. Put your mind for a moment on those you love and who have passed over. See them in your mind's eye and send them love.

4. Now put your mind on your enemies and those that have offended or hurt you. Send forgiveness to them and ask that they see the error of their ways.

5. Next, see those that you have hurt and ask them for forgiveness.

6. Put your mind upon your nearest and dearest in this life and send love to them.

7. Send out thoughts of love to all the animal kingdom and ask that those who torture or hurt animals realise that it is wrong and stop it.

8. Think of all suffering humanity and send out love.

9. See, in your mind, a picture of our beautiful, blue planet Earth, send out love and ask for forgiveness for the human race and for the damage we do to the environment.

10. Decide to help at least one person, animal or thing during this day.

11. Finally, ask that you learn at least one thing today.

Summary

- Meditation is a general term for a multitude of diverse types of practice.
- The purpose of meditation is to look within, enter the stillness and discover the self.
- Meditation can be subjective, objective, stilling or flowing. All of these qualities can apply at some time within all meditations.
- Meditators often report improvements in health and happiness, both physical and mental.

Chapter Twelve

Hypnosis And Trance

A kindly thought sent out, towards another human being;
Can guard the one receiving it, from sadness, hate and ruin.

There is plenty of evidence that the phenomenon of hypnotic trance has been used by humanity for eons.

What Is Hypnosis?
Many attempts to give a trite definition of this phenomenon have been made, yet still nobody can really state exactly what it is. It is probably more useful to describe more fully a few features of the hypnotic trance state, than attempt to define it. It is an altered state of consciousness, neither fully awake, nor fully asleep. During the trance, breathing may become deeper and the heart rate may decrease. The deeper in trance a person goes, the more strange and unusual the phenomenon. There may be no sensations of pain and often symptoms of illness can disappear. Long-term pain sufferers can learn to use trance to gain relief from suffering. Forgotten childhood memories may be recalled. People who stammer or stutter in the waking state may talk freely whilst in trance. Clinical or medical procedures may take place without anaesthetic or discomfort. Trance may also be used in the treatments of drug addiction and dependency.

Fears And Misconceptions
Is there a possibility that I might not awaken from hypnosis?
Hypnosis is not a kind of sleep, although it might appear so to anyone watching a subject in trance lying there with eyes closed, appearing to be well gone. Hypnosis can incorporate elements of relaxation and drowsiness. On the other hand, an alert vibrant state can just as easily be encouraged. A trance can be terminated simply by saying, `In a moment I want you to open your eyes wide-awake. Open your eyes now'. Immediately the subject will be able to open their eyes and return to a normal state of consciousness.

Can a hypnotist encourage me to do something bad against my will?
There have been several studies on this question and there are as
many `yes' as `no' answers. I have found that, in general, most
people will only accept suggestions that go along with their
personal ethical standards. However, if you are going for
hypnotherapy it is advisable to check that your therapist belongs
to a respectable national register of practitioners, one that has a
code of ethics and that can verify the standard of training that
your therapist has received. (See the useful address section.)

Do only weak minded people enter trance?
The opposite is true. The stronger-minded a person is, the more
able they are to enter trance. Remember, hypnosis is a form of
concentration; therefore, the "stronger" a mind is the more easily
it can reach a concentrated state. The average person is capable of
entering sufficiently deep enough states of hypnosis for effective
therapy to take place. I often meet people who say to me `I cannot
be hypnotised'. To these I say `Yes, I agree with you', and it is
true, for if someone resists suggestion then there is really no
chance of helping them to enter trance.

Does hypnosis weaken the mind?
Again, I would say that the opposite is true. Many student and
graduates use self-hypnosis to help them study and recall information as well as gain confidence to pass exams etc..

Can you make me tell you things that I would rather keep private?
There are two answers to this question. The first is that no ethical
hypnotherapist would even attempt to gain confidential information from you without first asking your permission prior to any
trance taking place. The second is that if a therapist attempted
this, it is likely that the critical censor in your conscious mind
would alert you and prevent anything happening.

Is it possible that when I am in trance I might slip into proper sleep?
This can happen. Of course when you are in normal sleep you
will leave the trance state. If you are working with a therapist he
or she would be aware that you had gone to sleep and would
either gently wake you or allow you to take a few moments' rest.
People only fall asleep from hypnosis if they are bored or
overtired.

Trance

Hypnotic trance is usually induced by firstly concentrating on a single idea until other thoughts become secondary and eventually merge into the background. At this point the door to the unconscious mind and its processes begins to open. This state of focus, of course, is not unique. Have you ever been reading something and someone has come and spoken to you? At that time you have been so absorbed in your reading that the first thing you know is when you hear that person say, `Hey, I have been speaking to you and you completely ignored me'. This state has no clear boundaries; there are elements of it in everything we do: when walking through the countryside lost in a reverie; just before dropping off to sleep in bed; doing breathing exercises; day-dreaming; driving a car; watching TV. These are just a few examples of altered trance-like states. Animals easily move from one trance state to another - watch your cat snoozing, it is always alert.

Trance And Sleep

We have discovered that hypnosis is neither full wakefulness nor full sleep. However, trance has some things in common with sleep:

- Trance suggestions can cause one to feel tired and relaxed.
- Dreamlike states may be encouraged when working through traumatic memory.
- When returning from a trance, suggestions may be given for forgetting anything that might cause discomfort at the conscious level. This is rather like waking up and forgetting the dreams you have just had.
- The word `sleep' is often used by hypnotists to begin trance.

The Unconscious Mind

In earlier chapters we discovered that the unconscious mind keeps us alive, stores information in memory, and is there to protect us from being bombarded consciously with too many stimuli. It is also the part that makes any changes that are suggested to it during hypnosis.

The unconscious part of the mind is far more open and susceptible to suggestion than the normal, logical, thinking conscious mind. It can accept suggestion without judgement and action things that the conscious mind would be sceptical or even cynical about.

We discovered that words could be used to influence feelings, emotions and pictures within the unconscious. In fact we discovered that the unconscious could be coaxed into accepting words as real things. Therefore, when the conscious mind is otherwise distracted or directed into a focal point, words can be subtly filtered past it into the unconscious for acceptance. Providing the words are acceptable to that person and do not in anyway challenge their ethical stance or belief systems, and that they wish for the outcome that is suggested, then the unconscious can get to work.

Time And The Unconscious Mind
Linear time means little to the unconscious, which is capable of processing and taking action upon suggestions or commands almost simultaneously. This accounts for reported miraculous or fantastic remissions from illness sometimes occurring soon after a suggestion is made. In his book, ***The Psychobiology Of Mind-Body Healing*** Ernest Rossi gives some examples of spontaneous remission. In trance, time becomes distorted and suggestions often encourage the unconscious to live through hours or days of trance time in a matter of minutes. For example, `Whilst you rest in this wonderful place/state, you may take as much time as you need in the next few moments to enjoy a full day of pleasurable healing rest'.

Who Hypnotises Who?
A good hypnotist will admit that the subject actually carries out the process. The hypnotist is a person who can speak in a special way to the subject's unconscious mind. The subject then either accepts the suggestions and goes into trance, or refuses to accept the suggestions and stays in their present state.

Self-Hypnosis
Teaching yourself self-hypnosis can have some minor difficulties. The problem is that a person is using their own conscious mind with all its scepticism to try to by-pass conscious thought processes, and at the same time asking the unconscious to carry out commands. These commands are likely to be ones that the

conscious mind has found difficult to work with itself. It is a kind of swings-and-roundabouts situation. I'm not saying that it doesn't work, but I have come across many people who admit to reading books on self-hypnosis and only gaining slight or little success when attempting to induce a hypnotic state.

There is a way, however, in which you can become capable of creating almost instant self-hypnosis. By making your own hypnotic induction audiotape you are able to plant post hypnotic suggestions in your mind whilst in trance. These suggestions could be that at some later time, when you are out of trance, you could carry out some function easily. In this case you are going to make suggestions that when you are out of trance, you will be able to use a simple word in a certain way and be able to quickly become self-hypnotised. Here is how to do this:

1. Get two tape recorders, one to record on and the other to play background music.

2. Put a blank tape in one and a music tape in the other.

3. Now have a quick look through the following script from START to FINISH before you begin to record it.

4. Then record the script whilst playing background music.

5. When the tape is made lie down and play it back to yourself.

6. Each day for the next week play the tape back to yourself until you know that you are able to enter trance without the tape.

7. A good idea is to attempt to put yourself into trance several times each day between playing the learning tape.

CAUTION: The tape you are about to make must not be listened to when operating machinery, when lying in the bath, or when driving a vehicle. Ideally find a place where you will be undisturbed whilst you listen to the tape. It must not be used if you are suffering any kind of psychological illness or disorder, such as clinical depression or any psychosis. If in doubt, always consult your doctor, specialist or consultant before using any techniques whatsoever from this book.

Hypnotic Tape Script
Now follows the self-hypnosis learning tape script.

Note: Pause for about five seconds between each statement; speak clearly and a little slower than normal.

START
Get yourself comfortable lying down or sitting; make sure that you are wrapped up warmly and unlikely to be disturbed for the next twenty minutes or so. Make sure that your head and neck are supported and that your body is in its most comfortable position. The secret keyword you choose should be one that you rarely use, maybe even a nonsense word that you make up and tell nobody about. However, it will only work if you use it as instructed and only when you personally intone it silently with the intent to enter trance.

- Now allow your whole body to become loose and limp. Pretend that you have no bones in your body.
- Make sure that your tummy muscles are floppy.
- If you have not already done so, close your eyes.
- Breathe gently and easily.
- If anything should happen during this session that requires your attention, you can easily open your eyes and get up and deal with it.
- Meanwhile, continue letting go of all tension in the head, face and neck.
- Let go of all tension in the shoulders, arms and hands.
- Let go of all tension in the thighs, legs and feet.
- Let go of all tension all the way down through your body, from the top of the head, all the way down to the tips of the toes.
- Very good.
- Now check the facial muscles are loose and elastic: in the forehead, in the eyes and around the eyes, the nose, cheeks and mouth.
- Notice how your face takes on a mask of no expression, easily, effortlessly. Good.
- Now just check that your spine is pliable and sink down into the chair/sofa/bed.
- Wonderful. Just allow the mind to drift, to find a memory of a wonderful experience.

- Perhaps you are in a place where you have enjoyed yourself, or an imaginary place, somewhere where you can see the sights, the shapes, in the colours that most relax you.
- Hear the pleasant sounds, feeling the temperature, maybe smell the attractive aroma; just let yourself enjoy it all.
- It might be a country place, or by the ocean, a lake, a river or a stream; whatever it is you can enjoy all these sensations. You might look up and see the blue sky like you've never seen it before, so beautiful, spreading out into eternity.
- Perhaps you can hear the sound of the soft breeze, or the water nearby as you just lie here and rest. That's really wonderful.
- Good; now just spend a few minutes enjoying going deeper and deeper into this wonderful experience.

Note: Here remain silent for two minutes, leave the background music playing. Then continue recording as follows:

- Now that you are enjoying this deep trance state, I want you to remind yourself of your secret word. This word is your signal to enter hypnosis, but only when you want to, and only when you use it in the following way. Whenever you wish to enter self-hypnosis this is what you will do:
- Sit down comfortably; close your eyes and take a deep, gentle breath, and as you breathe out gently and silently think of your secret word, and say silently after it, `I am now in self-hypnosis'.
- Whenever you do this you will immediately enter self-hypnosis and be in a deep trance, as you are now. The more often you practise this, the more easily you can enter self-hypnosis.
- Of course, whenever you wish to return from self-hypnosis back to the normal state you can simply say silently to yourself: "In a moment I will count from one up to five and when I reach five I will open my eyes, wide awake, feeling comfortable, relaxed and refreshed, and ready to get on with my life."
- Then you will count one, two, three, four, five, and then open your eyes. Don't rush to get up; just spend a few moments to check that you are back to full consciousness, feeling really comfortable and wide awake.

- Good, just spend a few more minutes in this wonderful safe place of yours, remembering that whenever you wish to return here you can simply put yourself into trance and be here, or you can put yourself into trance and be somewhere else that you will enjoy.

Note: At this point in the recording keep quiet for two minutes, just leave the background music playing. Then continue recording as follows:

- Now it's time to let yourself leave this place and slowly return, until you find yourself back in familiar surroundings, sitting or lying here, having feelings of comfort and relaxation.
- OK, in a few moments' time I will count from one up to five and as I count each number you will come further up out of this trance feeling refreshed, comfortable and relaxed, and ready to get on with your life.
- Are you ready? One; two, coming, up feeling really good; three, half-way up; four, your conscious mind is once more in full control of all your body; five, when you are ready and only then slowly, easily and effortlessly open your eyes, wide awake.
- Don't rush to get up; just take your time and when you feel ready get up and get on with your life.

FINISH

Note: this tape should take approximately twenty to twenty-five minutes to record.

How To Use The Tape

Once the tape is made, rewind it and just lie down. Get comfortable and then listen to the instructions that you have given yourself on this tape. It will put you into a deeply relaxed state and each time you use it, you improve and reinforce your ability to enter self-hypnosis. Do this for several days once or twice a day until your unconscious mind allows you to enter trance simply by taking a breath and using your secret word. After using the tape attempt to put yourself back into trance by using your secret word.

When you are able to self-induce hypnosis you will be an accomplished self-hypnotist. You can relax or use silent affirmations and visualisations as described in Chapter Four. This will enhance the effects of those suggestions and pictures.

Other Scripts

You can make scripts up yourself and then tape them. Good hypnotists realise that in order to make the most effective suggestions, they should use the subject's own terms of reference. In this case you are both the therapist and the subject, and from this you will realise that you are perhaps the most effective communicator to work with your unconscious mind. There are two simple tips before attempting to make your own therapy scripts:

- Speak clearly and just slightly more slowly than normal.
- Use positive statements, rather than negative ones, similar to the affirmations in Chapter Four.

A Healing Script

Healing scripts are very useful because everyone that comes for therapy requires some relief from a pain, problem, relationship or situation. Healing can cover all or any of these types of changes. So here is a typical healing script either to use as it is or to adapt for your particular situation, and then record it. Later you can use it as often as you want simply by sitting or lying down and listening to it.

START

- Get yourself comfortable, either sitting or lying, wrapped up warmly, with your head and neck supported.
- Make sure that you are in a place where you are unlikely to be disturbed.
- If anything does happen during this session, however, that requires your personal attention, you can open your eyes easily, wide awake, and get up and deal with whatever it is.
- Now close your eyes and take a nice deep breath; hold it a moment and then gently exhale. Good.
- Now make sure that your tummy muscles are loose and limp so that you can breathe easily without any tension.
- Put your attention on your head and be aware of all the little scalp muscles becoming loose and pliable. Good.
- Now allow those feelings to flow down from the top of your head into the back of your head and neck, and down the sides of the head and neck. Wonderful.
- Now check your facial muscles, forehead, all the little muscles in and around the eyes, all loose and limp; let go of all tension; feel those sensations flowing into the nose, mouth and big jaw muscles. Fine.
- Now be aware of your face taking on a mask of no expression as every muscle becomes elastic and pliable.
- Breathing gently and easily, just feel your shoulders slump, your arms and hands become heavy, loose, limp, comfortable.
- Now be aware of your whole body as if there are no bones in it; your body slumps down, comfortably loose, into the chair/sofa/bed, your thighs are loose and heavy and the knees, shins and calves are floppy; be aware of this gentle relaxation spreading down into the ankles and on down into the feet and toes. Very good.
- Now just lie there listening to the music, breathing gently and easily and just letting your mind drift into any happy memory, anywhere you want; good; seeing the sights, the colours, hearing the gentle sounds, and feeling the perfect temperature; you might even be aware of pleasant aromas or even tastes, whatever it is about the situation that helps you to enjoy the sensations.

Note: Here remain silent for two minutes whilst the tape continues recording the background music. Then continue speaking as follows:

- Good. Now imagine somewhere above your head a cloud of golden, scintillating light just glowing with healing vibrance.
- In a moment I am going to say the word `NOW' and when I do, I want you to be aware of that golden, healing light flowing down onto your head and flowing through your whole being, with healing, soothing energy.
- Ready, ready, NOOOOOWWWWWWW.
- Good, feel that golden light flooding through you, soothing, healing, moving all dark patches; just lie there as the golden healing light fills you with healing energy.

Note: Here stop speaking and let the tape continue recording the background music. Then continue speaking as follows:

- Now, feel the golden light flowing out of your feet, taking with it all impurities.
- As the golden light leaves, you feel yourself filling with beautiful, white light.
- Be aware of your body filling with this soothing, healing, white light.

Note: Here pause from speaking, let the tape continue recording the background music.

- Good, now feel the white light fading and as it does you can feel yourself refreshed and very comfortable.

Note: Again remain silent for a minute or two, leave the tape recording the background music. Then continue as follows:

- In a few moments time I will count from one up to ten and as I do you can leave this pleasant place, remembering that you can return here whenever you want, simply by getting comfortable and relaxing.

- So when you are ready; one, coming up; two; three; four, feeling comfortable; five, half-way up; six; seven; eight, feeling calm, relaxed and refreshed; nine, your conscious mind is once more in full control of every part of your body; ten. When you are ready and only then slowly, easily and effortlessly open your eyes, wide awake.
- Don't rush to get up, just stay there for a few moments, have a yawn and a stretch and then when you are ready, get up and get on with your life. Good!

FINISH

Final Word

I hope that you enjoy using these techniques for your own personal pleasure. This does not make you a therapist or a qualified hypnotist, so do not try to hypnotise anyone else. If you wish to use hypnosis or hypnotherapy there are some wonderful training organisations available in the UK and the US. I will have included the names of some at the end of this book.

Summary

- Hypnosis is an altered state of consciousness. It is not sleep and it is not ordinary wakefulness.
- It is usually induced by concentrating on a single idea.
- When the conscious mind is thus distracted the door to the unconscious is opened.
- The unconscious mind is not judgmental and accepts suggestions that the conscious mind might be sceptical about.
- Words and phrases can be as real to the unconscious as real situations.
- The unconscious works in the here-and-now and can work outside time restrictions as we know them.
- Most hypnotists would admit that generally a subject hypnotises him/herself by accepting suggestions from the hypnotist. Most hypnosis is therefore self-hypnosis to a degree.
- However, to actually talk oneself into trance can be difficult, as the conscious mind becomes involved and often prevents true trance to occur.
- By making a self-hypnosis tape with post-hypnotic suggestions included it is possible to plant a trigger word, phrase or symbol which can be used to enter self-hypnosis almost instantly and at any time.
- You must never attempt to hypnotise anyone, unless you have been properly trained by a reputable organisation.

Chapter Thirteen

Karma, Reincarnation And Past Lives

I sense deathlessness within; I know a part of me did not begin;
In this or any other life's attire; But is unending never to expire.

Karma

Karma can be best described as the law of causation, balance and compensation. The person who carries out an action becomes the attractor for a similar action. This law applies not only to human beings, but also to all creatures and things. In Chapter Four we learned that in nature, for every force exerted there is an equal and opposite force. Applying this to human life, it seems to indicate that even when someone dies with unfinished business it needs to be eventually addressed. This certainly helps to explain how we can experience several lives.

Karma does not work in a punitive sense though. It is there to help growth and evolution to take place. Liz Hodgkinson (1989) says,

> *"Hindus take the idea of Karma, or cause and effect, very seriously. In simple terms, this doctrine teaches that whatever we do in one life will have an inevitable consequence."*

It works like strands intertwining between people, nations, countries, etc. Therefore, when someone is born it is important that they fit in with the Karma of their relationships. By relationships I mean family, friends, towns and countries and also that particular time in history.

Karma takes into consideration action, reaction, compromise and retribution. It is there solely to guide, correct, direct and reward all actions. Once we have learned a lesson the Karma is released. Karma can be delayed from one life to another. Sometimes only portions of a past life's Karma are filtered through in accordance with how much that person is capable of working and coping with it. Nature rarely overloads anyone with more Karma than they are capable of dealing with at any one time. Some Karma can be paid within the same lifetime as it is accrued.

As we reach higher states of consciousness through spiritual evolution, Karma becomes more immediate. Some people do a thing and almost immediately the corrective force of Karma intervenes and that person is hopefully led to adjust there and then. I have been talking of Karma as if it is some kind of punishment; remember, it can be positive and pleasurable as well as corrective and unpleasant.

The Personality
In Chapter One I mentioned that each of us has a spirit or life-spark, a mind or conscious awareness, and a body. Let us consider the spirit and the intuitive higher part of the mind together. Here we have a conscious awareness above the personality; this we might call the soul. We are still left with the lower parts - the lower mind using the brain as a physical computer, and the physical body. In my case, I call these elements Tom Bolton - me as a personality.

Between the soul and the personality imagine a kind of overlap, a part that we could call a bridge, a kind of feeling that I am more than just a body and a brain. A feeling of I AM.

Death
At some point in time the real me (the soul) will decide that the earth vehicle (my body and brain plus personality) have served their purpose on this earth. Then the life signal will stop and physical death will occur.

The lower brain will at the moment of death pass all of Tom Bolton's life information up into the soul. Thus Tom Bolton will no longer exist on this earth. However, my full memory of this earth life will be preserved within my soul memory.

A Scenario Of Between Life States

As I expire from physical life, I am given a short spell of rest. During this rest period my soul can put the Tom Bolton life memories onto the "hard drive" memory with all its other earth lives throughout time. Next is likely to come an introspective inquiry into the events of Tom Bolton's life on the earth plain. The negative, self-destructive and damaging elements will be examined. During this examination there is likely to be a feeling of judgement, albeit self-judgement, and a feeling of regret that these things were not worked through before death occurred. Some form of notation is made so that in future lives these lessons need retaking and working through.

Next, the positive elements will be examined and there will be feelings of happiness and joy. These elements can be recorded as learnings useful as future strengths. They will be gifts in future lives. My soul now enters a level of consciousness suitable to it for reflection, assimilation and between life learnings. During this period it is likely that other souls of similar vibration will interact with my soul. This level of conscious awareness is likely to be almost unrestricted because at this mental and soul level, imagery and imagination are likely to create whatever I wish to see or be. Beyond linear time, instant action follows thought. Other souls from my Karmic group, relatives, friends from Tom Bolton's life and from my soul's other lives are likely to interact with me here. There is no physical pain so those who suffered on earth are pain-free here. They are likely to look young and vibrant. Souls are likely to reincarnate in groups, so a soul that was my mum in a Tom Bolton's life, might in my next life be an aunt, father, sister, brother, one of my children, or even a friend or any family member in past lives. Not all souls in a group reincarnate every time in the same lives. This is because we are all learning at different speeds.

The earth is the classroom where time is taken to do things, so that through time we can evolve and learn.

Reincarnation

After a period of rest and reflection in the heaven-life with loved ones, the time comes around when the soul gets an urge to return. It's a kind of spiritual frustration. Too much of a good thing can get boring. A new scenario begins:

The soul now decides to consider another earth life; there are still many lessons to be learned on the path of spiritual evolution. By now, the soul has detected suitable conditions down on earth for further learning and working through outstanding lessons. These conditions take into consideration a mother, her circumstances and Karmic links.

The mother is the most vital Karmic link, because all the other environmental effects are conditioned by her presence on earth. These will include: my next human incarnation, name, time and date of birth, place of birth, country of origin, who is to be my father, my relatives, my home life, my early upbringing, my first contact with others, types of food medical care; etc.. Can you see how the mother is the most important part of earthly life's Karma.

If the time of birth is not synchronised correctly then the soul must cause a premature or late birth to ensure that I arrive in my new personality, so that the stage is set to allow my new personality every opportunity to optimise learning.

On occasions environmental conditions might alter and make this the wrong time or place. In this type of situation the soul sometimes aborts and there is still-birth. Whatever happens it will fit in with the mother's Karma. Remember Karma applies to everyone.

Karma's Effect On Reincarnation

Reincarnation occurs because of the leftover effects of Karma or the ever-turning wheel of life. When a soul is reincarnated, it projects into the new life the leftover effects of Karma from its previous incarnations. The latest personality will have some of the earned strengths and benefits from previous lives, and it will also incur some of the negative qualities and effects from the previous cycle of lives, to be used as fuel for learning in the new incarnation.

You might think this seems unfair, but it's no more unfair than a relay team passing the baton on to the next runner. If the previous members of that relay team had gained time, then the present runner starts off ahead of the race. If, however, the team had lost time, the present runner would have to try that much harder in order to catch up, or to get on. It's not the person who is winning or losing, it is the team.

Likewise a soul is like the team leader. The team is the stream of incarnations that the soul has initiated. The personalities are the members of the soul team. When that soul has worked through all the binding Karma accrued throughout all its earth lives, liberation can then occur. After liberation the soul needs no further incarnations on earth but lives in the higher realms of consciousness. However some souls look back to the earth and see suffering humanity; they decide to come back to help others. These people we call the Great Masters, Avatars or Buddhas.

Jesus was a wonderful example of a perfect soul. He was truly the Son of God. But he never claimed to be the only Son of God. Jesus considered that we are all sons and daughters of God.

Regressions

A devout religious man once came to me and asked me to help him discover some of his previous-life experiences. His first regression took him back to the Middle Ages. Here he was the Abbot of a hidden brotherhood of monks. At that time monks were being persecuted and the Roman Catholic Church was under persecution from the reformers. On this day he was sitting at the head of a long bench; it was a mealtime and all the brothers were eating. Their meal consisted of vegetables, mainly beets of some kind. The Abbot was enjoying a game bird. I asked him if he believed in God and he answered that he was not sure. I then asked him why he was an Abbot if he had such doubts. His reply was that he had power and good food.

The next regression for this man took him to a dingy London street on a misty winter's night in the seventeen hundreds. He was dressed like a gentleman. Just ahead of him was an older man who had just alighted from a passing carriage. Our gentleman followed the man down an alley and coshed him viciously. He then relieved him of his coinage and valuables before disappearing into the dark. Soon he arrived at a gentleman's club. Here, in front of a roaring fire, he sat with other fellow thieves who were boasting of their night's plundering. An unsuspecting servant, who they referred to as "the old boy", treated them to some hot alcoholic drinks. On returning back here this man was aghast at what he had found out. In his present life he is a dedicated Buddhist; in at least two of his past lives he was a person of ill-repute.

Wasps

A young married lady aged twenty-eight came to me suffering from a phobia of wasps. She had always been very wary of wasps, but now the fear was becoming unbearable. She also admitted to being over protective of her six-year-old daughter and petrified that she might be stung. She made sure that her daughter never left her sight, even in the home. If she heard any buzzing, even from a fly, she would feel the fear building up inside her. We did the usual phobia cure and therapy. She went away apparently feeling OK. On her next visit she said the fear was building again. We decided to try regression. She went back to being a young girl in this life playing in the field with her brothers. The boys were climbing up some trees and as she watched them, she put her hand on a fence post and on top of a wasp which stung her. She ran home screaming and her mum gave her loads of kisses and fuss and put some ointment on the sting. After this therapy she felt OK and went home.

A week later she was back again, the phobia was building and she was getting even more protective over her daughter. We decided to try a past-life regression and with the help of her unconscious mind we asked it to locate any incident in any time that had some bearing on how she had learned to have this terribly increasing phobia. She found herself as a Dutch mother about two hundred years ago, out for a walk with her daughter. The little girl, aged six, ran off into the bushes. The mum heard some screaming and ran quickly into the bushes. There she found her little daughter had fallen into a wasp's or hornets' nest and was lying on the floor screaming as many of them stung her. The child was so badly stung that she soon died, and the mother cried and cried and spoke words I couldn't understand.

When my client awoke from hypnosis she felt a great relief. She talked of feeling so sorry that the little girl had died. On the next visit she was fine, the phobia had completely gone, she felt less over-protective of her own little daughter, and things were going well at home.

Soul Mates

A young man of thirty-two asked me to help him to regress. We were to allow his unconscious mind to take him to any previous life he might have had. His lady friend who was from Hong Kong asked if she could sit in. I told her that after I had induced him into trance I would call her into the room. The young man was soon in trance and I brought his girlfriend into the room. She sat there and seemed to drift into trance as well. The young man found himself in an earlier time some three hundred years ago. He was in a coaching inn, and he spoke of enjoying his drink and talking to some friends. He mentioned some things about the way the people spoke and what they were saying. This went on for some time and when he was ready to return I brought him back. We then began to discuss some of the things that he had seen that he had not mentioned whilst in trance.

As he was talking about a person who was at the inn, his girlfriend said, "You were dressed in a green suite, with a black cape and long brown boots".

The young man looked quite shaken and said, "How do you know that; I haven't mentioned how I was dressed?"

"I was there."

He then said to her, "I felt that I knew there was someone there from my present life. Were you the lady in the bonnet and long purple overcoat standing near the door looking at me?"

It was her turn to look aghast. It turned out that she had apparently slipped into trance whilst I was working with her boyfriend, and had experienced his regression. She had actually been there with him in that life. She, of course, was not his girlfriend then, just someone who felt attracted to him. Incidentally, in that life she was not from Hong Kong, she was French.

Gender

A young lady came to see me and asked to be regressed to a previous life. She said she had a gender problem and wanted to find out why. She would tell me no more than this. She insisted that, when she was regressed, I help her facilitate the therapy without asking too many questions. I agreed to this and helped her regress in a way that did not require much input from me. I made sure that she was comfortable, not trapped in a traumatic situation. We asked her unconscious to help her go back through time to find the time or incident that would clarify for her the situation referred to. She went back through time from one life to another, visiting several past existences. She did not wish to share much of what happened. She did however tell me that her last five incarnations were as a man. The first of these was a gender crisis in a male body. Through the next few sessions we went back further and found that, before that other crises, she had been through a series of lives as a female.

After that session she said she no longer had any worries about herself and had come to terms with her feeling about her gender. I'll leave you to form your own conclusions about this situation.

These are just a few simple examples of past lives. There are hundreds more.

Summary

- Karma is the law of causation, balance and compensation.
- The soul is the immortal part of us.
- The personality lives on earth for the soul to experience and learn from.
- Death is just the casting off of the earthly body.
- Between lives the soul assimilates the learnings from each lifetime.
- Reincarnation occurs when the self again thirsts for earthly experience.
- Past-life regressions help to show how people evolve through a series of lives.

Aphorisms From The Ageless Wisdom

Here I have included some notes I made during my studies of the Ageless Wisdom between 1985 and 1990. I have found them of great help to me on my journey. I hope you will get as much joy from reading through them as I do.

Wisdom from above transforms life.
A good deed, however small, will benefit someone.
Be a channel for peaceful forces.
Endeavour to live in harmony with nature and your neighbours.
Listen to your intuition.
Keep the light in sight; even when taking a wrong turn, look
for the light.
Live serenely in spite of difficulties.
Live like a seed; the force is within.
Not what I was in the past; or what I am at present; but what I strive for
in the future.
Don't store information, use it.
Experience is the best learning.
Lead your life and wisdom will come naturally.
Speaking is easily done; doing is harder.
Gravity is the weakest of forces yet it holds the universe together.
Nothing happens by chance.
The brave person picks him/herself up after each defeat.
The divine self shows its weakest parts outward when
in incarnation.
True love does not try to alter others.
There is no true perfection in this world.
Be careful how you influence others. Through egotism you can
incur Karma.
Those who never ask anything but love, have Gods home in
their hearts.
Desire to sow no seed for your own harvest; rather desire to
sow a seed for the world.
God is life and love; recognition of this fact is spiritual
consciousness.
Grow as the flower grows, unconsciously, but eager to open its
soul to the air.

Everything needs time appropriate to its own nature, and
time to complete its allotted task.
The universe exists for the Self.
In life you make your choice and pay your dues.
Sin is missing the target.
Life will shut you down until you go in the right direction.
Take the little opportunities and this will lead to bigger ones.
If you feel you've lost an opportunity, look for the next.
Whatever you truly love you cannot lose.
Whatever you think of in the universe, you have a rapport with.
It is good for our souls to be found out.
Fears are not now, but what might happen, and often doesn't.
I am the captain of my soul. I am the master of my fate.
Look upon every situation as an opportunity for development.
Pull out the weeds, then stop planting more.
Each person is her/his absolute lawgiver.
Character is an event, a legacy of the past.
None but us compel.
Sow a thought to reap a habit; then the habit reaps a character; finally
the character reaps destiny.
Become in practice what you are in potential.
Always remember that you are bigger than the passing hour and
anything it brings.
Endeavour to live now in the ever-present eternal.
There are no foes, no friends; all alike are my teachers.
Have things but do not be tied to them.
When a sensation comes, enjoy it then let it go.
Deal with each person as they are.
Don't condemn, don't patronise, and don't be indifferent.
If you have to criticise do it without blame or praise.

Chapter Fourteen

Conclusion

In our journey together through this book we have looked at several different forms of vibration. We have learned that moderation in all things leads to balance and equilibrium. In human terms this requires that we do the following:

- Respond to stressors in effective ways.
- Be aware of signs of overload and immediately take the necessary action to release stress.
- Be aware that pains and disease are signals that we are out of balance with nature.
- Take sufficient rest, recreation and exercise.
- Take in sufficient quantities of quality air, water and food.
- Ensure that we are have a balanced intake of vitamins and minerals.
- Take proper care of our bodies.
- Do some form of meditation.
- Remember that prayer is very powerful; however it is not just asking for things for you.

The most effective prayer is when you are asking for something for another person. Never forget to say "thank you" when praying, and always expect your prayers to be answered.

My Beliefs

I was sitting in a cafe today talking to my friend Roy. We were very briefly discussing star signs and characteristics of Taurians. Roy said, "Do you really belief in all that stuff?" I had to admit that I had certainly noticed traits and relationships that seemed to verify some truth within Astrology. I have learned never to close my mind upon any subject. I realise that such subjects as Karma, reincarnation, religion, types of healing, etc. can be controversial. My only firm, unmoving personal belief is that there are no firm yes and nos about anything. Surely in our universe, which is a magnificent expression of multiple dimensions of infinity, there must be room for unlimited expressions of life. I further believe that, as three dimensional thinkers, we are restricted in the ways that we describe our beliefs.

Maybe several people arguing over an idea could all be right and all be wrong at the same time. Here is a little story just to illustrate my point:

The Adventurers And The Elephant
Four adventurers went to India many years ago. They had heard about a giant creature called an elephant, but none had yet seen one. A local prince invited them to his palace for some fun. He told them he had a perfect specimen to show them, and took them out to a massive building in his garden. There were four doors in the building, one on each side. Each adventurer was invited to be blindfolded and to enter the building, one through each entrance. Afterwards, the blindfolds were removed and they were asked what they had discovered.

The first adventurer said that she was sure that the elephant must be like a big hosepipe. She had felt its trunk.

The second adventurer said he thought it was like four tree trunks. He had felt its legs.

The third adventurer said she was certain that the elephant was like a big boulder. She had stroked its body.

The fourth adventurer said that they were all wrong; the elephant was like a huge leaf. He had felt one of its ears.

Later the prince had a servant lead the elephant out into the sunlight. All of the adventurers were astonished. They each realised how limited their view was. Who was right? They all were, of course, but only relatively. They were also completely wrong; they hadn't described all the magnificent dimensions of that elephant. This is paradox.

When you enter the world of self-discovery you come across paradox more and more. It's therefore important not to cast aside something that at this moment in time you are not ready to understand. As a therapist I have to be fairly open-minded and enter the belief systems of my clients in order to help them open up more alternatives for themselves.

One Last Word

If we are to survive on this wonderful planet of ours we need to take care of it. Like us, the planet can suffer from overloads of stress. The ozone layer is getting thinner every year; the ice caps are melting; freak weather is becoming more common and the air and seas are increasingly less pure.

It is time we made balance and moderation the normal rather than the exception to the rule. To find harmony with our earth we must first look within ourselves, and gain wholeness and equilibrium. I hope this book will help you do just that.

Just before I say goodbye here is a little poem that came to me one night as I was about to fall asleep. I decided to get up and write it down.

Tips Along Life's Way

Be a channel for peaceful forces, try to mirror harmony;
Listen to your intuition, send out thoughts of purity.
Never ponder on your past, or wonder what you are to be.
Always live now in the present, being kind to all you see.

Have ambition for all creation, cast off pride and selfishness.
Give free help without concession; do not act like all the rest.
Fill your life, be always learning, this way wisdom can flow through.
Cultivate a sense of humour; invite all to laugh with you.

Treat your sorrows with detachment and those pleasures just the same;
Soon you'll see they are illusions, trials to test you in life's game.
What you do is meant to happen, nothing is by chance or free;
Joys and sorrows, peace and turmoil, all these things were meant to be.

Finale

Well, dear reader, I wish you great happiness. I hope that you will not only read this book through, over and over again, but also apply the information and use some of the techniques from it in your daily life. They will, I am sure, help you as they have helped me to `Vibrate with Health and Happiness'.

Bibliography

Heyn, Birgit. (1987) *Ayurvedic Medicine*. U.K. Thorsons Publishers Ltd.

Humphreys, Naomi. (1987) *Meditation: The Inner Way*. Scotland, U.K. William Collins & Sons.

Johanson, Tom. (1986) *Release Your Inner Healing Power*. U.K. Bishopgate Press Ltd.

Hodgkinson, Liz. (1989) *Reincarnation: The Evidence*. U.K Judy Piatkus (Publishers) Ltd.

Ouseley, S.G. (1986) *Colour Meditations*. U.K. L. N. Fowler & Co Ltd.

Rossi, E.l. (1986) *The Psychobiology Of Mind-Body Healing*. New York, U.S.A. and London, U.K. Norton & Co Ltd.

Smith, E & Wilks, N. (1988) *Meditation (Alternative Health)*. U.K. Macdonald (Optima).

International Bible Society. (1988) *The Holy Bible (New International Version)*. Hodder & Stoughton.

Further Reading

Apple, Michael. (1997) *How To Stay Healthy*. London, U.K. Bloomsbury Publishing Plc.

Atkinson, Jacqueline. (1994) *Coping With Stress At Work*. London, UK. Thorsons.

Campbell, Anthony. (1991) *Natural Health*. London, UK. New Burlington Books.

Chaitow, Leon. (1990) *Clear Body Clear Mind*. UK. Unwin Paperbacks.

Earle, Liz. (1991) *Vital Oils*. London, UK. Centuary Vermilion.

Harold, Edmond. (1986) *Crystal Healing* UK. Thorsons Group.

Lalvani, Villa. (1995) *Yogacise*. London, UK. Hamlyn Books.

Meredith, Bronwen. (1984) *Stay Younger Longer*. London, UK. Elmtree Books.

Ornstein, R., & Sobel, D. (1988) *The Healing Brain*. London, UK. Macmillan.

Peel, Robert. (1987) *Spiritual Healing In A Scientific Age*. San Francisco, USA. Harper and Row.

Powell, Allen. (1988) (Revised by Dr Tag Powell). *As You Thinketh*. Florida, USA. Top of the Mountain.

Smith, Trevor. Dr. (1986) *Emotional Health*. London, UK. Insight Books.

Taylor, Allegra. (1987) *I Fly Out With Bright Feathers*. London, UK. CW Daniel Co.

Turner, Roger Newman. (1994) *Naturopathic Medicine.* London, UK.

Worwood, Valerie. A/ (1995) *Fragrant Mind.* London, UK. Bantam.

Youngson, Robert. Dr. (1994) *Antioxidant Health Play.* London, UK. Thorsons.

Glossary Of Terms

Affirmation: An assertion designed to stimulate a positive inner response, leading to the attainment of a goal.

Ajna: An energy centre corresponding to the mid-eyebrow point.

Anahata: An energy centre corresponding to the area of the thymus gland and heart.

Aphorism: A concise, essential seed statement designed to stimulate thought at profound levels of mind.

Aromatherapy: Treatments using hormonal plant extracts to stimulate healing processes.

Brain: The thinking, storing, organising organ of the mind. An organic super computer.

Carbohydrates: A compound of carbon, oxygen and hydrogen. Powerful ,quick-release energy source.

Chakras: Wheels of light; energy centres; transformers of psychic energy.

Crystals: Quartz and mineral life forms. They vibrate on frequencies healthful to life. Often used for some healing and meditation practices.

Concentration: To focus the mind on an object, idea or thought.

Constitution: A physical condition or state.

Creative visualisation: To see within the mind a beneficial condition, state or situation, and through this vision stimulate the necessary action to realise it.

Cosmic Rays: Universal colour spectrum of radiant energies.

Death: A time when the body is shed. The cessation of an organic life.

Diet: The intake of nourishment in the form of food and drink.

Digestion: The process of breaking food down into its components for assimilation within the body.

Doshas: Nature's three principal forces of balance and equilibrium. They are Vata, Pitta and Kapha.

Earth:	Our world, a planet in the Solar System.
Electricity:	Vibrating waves of energy which can produce the phenomena of heat, light and sound.
Essential oils:	Vital hormonal life-giving essences which are extracted from plants, usually by distillation.
Ether:	Space; the womb of all potential; the unified field of all possibility.
Existence:	Material being.
Fats:	Acids containing hydrogen and oxygen, attached to chains of carbon atoms.
Feelings:	Sensations created by contact,; also emotional states.
Fibre:	Essential indigestible bulk, valuable to humans as a purgative. Found in cereals, pulses and most fruit and vegetables.
Goals:	Objectives to aim for.
God:	The supreme absolute spirit.
Healing:	Returning to a healthy, balanced state.
Healer:	One who channels energy into a sick person, animal or plant in order to improve health.
Holistic:	The whole thing, as a whole.
Hypnosis:	An altered state of consciousness, which allows direct communications with the unconscious inner processes of mind.
Ida:	Psychic channel through which female/moon energy flows.
Illness:	A state of imbalance.
Kundilini:	The vital force residing in the Base Chakra. Said to be coiled three and a half times.
Life:	Period of existence in plants, animals and humans.
Love:	This term has many meanings, generally an intense spiritual experience between two or more beings.
Manipura:	A chakra located in the solar plexus area.

Mantra:	A sound for use during some meditative and contemplative practices. It is said to have several qualities which can benefit the user.
Meditation:	A reflective state of deep rest or contemplation, often leading to transcendence of the thinking process.
Mind:	A pool of consciousness stirred by vibrations of thought.
Muladhara:	A chakra located at the base of the spine, here Kundilini resides.
Nervous system:	The communication network of the mind and body.
Past-life regression:	When someone apparently moves back through time in thought and re-experiences events not from their present life.
Personality:	The make-up, attitudes and personal traits of a person. Personal identity.
Pingala:	The psychic channel that carries male energy down the right side; often referred to as the Sun channel.
Pitta:	One of nature's balancing forces.
Rajas:	A primary quality of matter, activity, emotion, feeling, passion.
Reincarnation:	When a soul forms a new life on earth through a personality.
Sahasrara:	A subtle point above and beyond other chakras; it corresponds to the crown of the head.
Sattva:	The most subtle spiritual primary quality of matter, balance, existence, essence, being, true life, light.

Senses: Parts and organs connected through the nervous system to the mind. They interpret their own frequencies of vibrations and, through the brain, reflect them as feeling, emotions, sight, taste, smell, hearing. They sense external and internal stimulation.

Stress: Pressure often causing friction or tension.

Stress overload: An unsatisfactory state of intense strain or discomfort, often leading to disorders, illness and disease.

Stressors: Provokers of response, sometimes leading to stress-overload situations if not dealt with or responded to.

Sushumna: A primary psychic channel that runs from the Base Chakra straight up to the Ajna - Brow Chakra. Only activated when Ida and Pingala are unblocked.

Svadhisthana: Chakra located about two inches below the navel.

Synergy: When two or more ingredients join up. Their interaction increases the effectiveness of both. The total effect is more than the sum of the individual contributions.

Tamas: One of three primary qualities of matter; inertia, lethargy, darkness, solidness.

Tastes: Qualities in nature usually attributed to foods. They are: sweet, sour, salty, pungent, bitter, astringent.

Therapy: Treatments to help a person cope and/or recover from a problem, illness, etc.

Trance: An altered state often associated with hypnosis or daydreaming.

Unconscious mind: All mind processes beyond and outside present awareness.

Vata: A natural principal of kinetic energy.

Vital force: A power within every atom and cell of the body.

Visuddha: Chakra situated at the base of the throat.

Vitamins: Essential trace elements found in foods and sunlight.

About The Author

Clients often ask me how I came to be a therapist. I tell them that my own suffering had a lot to do with it.

I was born in Devonport in England on 1st of September, 1940. My dad, Lance, was a stoker in the Royal Navy and my mum, Winnie, was a demonstrator. My first few years of life were spent living in a boarding house close to the dockyard. Devonport was often blitzed and I slept in a suitcase so that when the sirens went mum could rush with me down to the safety of the shelters.

When I was three, mum took me to live in Bolton, Lancashire with Nana and Granddad. Those were happy times. In 1946, dad returned from sea and was demobbed. He took mum and me to live in Wirral, Cheshire. Dad was suffering mentally from the effects of war; he was moody and didn't have much time for children. My brother, Vince and sister, Rosemary were born in 1947. As a family, we lived in one set of rooms after another, until in 1949 we were given a council house in Moreton, Wirral. We were not very well off as Dad was in and out of work.

Mum and Dad seemed to be always arguing. I would often wake up at night, listening to Mum screaming and shouting, whilst Dad kept up a barrage of sarcastic remarks. They had absolutely nothing in common: Mum was a highly emotional, excitable person, whilcst Dad was a person who didn't like to show his feelings. Mum was a Roman Catholic and dad was an agnostic. He was very strict and I was a mischievous child. Because of this I was forever being punished, not physically but mentally. I was sent to bed early, had no pocket money, was not allowed to play out with my friends for months at a time. The punishments were really over the top.

In addition to this my mother had poor health and often had to go into hospital for major operations. I was given the responsibility of looking after my twin brother and sister aswell as running the house. When I was eleven, Mum and Dad separated. Life became bearable at last. There was no bickering, no punishment; we were poor but happy. Mum worked at three part-time jobs to provide for us. One day, when I was fifteen, Mum said, 'Your Dad is sorry for the past; he would like to come back home'. That's when I decided to leave.

In 1956 I joined the Royal Navy and was trained as a communicator at HMS in Suffolk. I spent the next fourteen years travelling the world. I was often very moody and aggressive, drank too much and smoked like a chimney. During this time I married Mary and had three sons.

I left the service in 1970 and had a series of jobs in retail, management, milk delivery, painting and decorating, and was finally unemployment. Through this time stress overload had badly affected my life, and my relationship with my wife and those around me. In 1977 I was divorced. I then went though several years of depression, anxiety and heavy drinking. My relationships were stormy and short-lived.

By 1983 I was unemployed and had for several years suffered from stomach ulcers, panic attacks, anxiety and deep depression. I was taking medication to help me sleep and tranquilizers for the anxiety and panic attacks, but medication only seem to make things worse. Then one day someone taught me a simple meditative technique. After a few days I felt less stressed and began to sleep better at nights. I continued meditating twice daily, and began some special stretching exercises, and discovered various other techniques for releasing stress. Soon the panic attacks stopped and the depression began to lift. I then joined a group of students of the Ageless Wisdom and discovered the holistic approach to life. (Even now I continue to be an avid investigator into these ancient secrets).

As time went on, my life became more settled and healthy. This made me sensitively aware of the suffering of others in the world around me. At that point, I made the decision to spend the rest of my life helping those less fortunate than myself. For the next few years I studied and gained qualifications in psychotherapy, hypnotherapy and holistic practices. In addition to this I voluntarily counselled alcoholics, tutored handicapped adults, and carried out many hours of unpaid therapy work.

In 1990 I met Beverley. We now live happily together in Wallasey, Wirral. We are both members of the World Federation of Healing. I use hypnotherapy, psychotherapy and healing in my work and have developed some very effective ways of treating many conditions. I call these collectively `Remission Target Therapy'. RTT offers people quick, short, effective ways to improve their quality of life. Using RTT I am able to help healthy people to gain confidence, learn to relax, set and achieve goals, overcome examination nerves, sleep well at night, cope effectively with the challenges of modern life, remove phobias, improve memory, give up smoking, and use imagination usefully as a tool for success. RTT is also helpful in offering relief from many painful and distressful conditions such as, anxiety, depression, phobias, post traumatic stress disorder, behavioral problems, compulsive and obsessive states, insomnia, learning difficulties, pain management, alcohol addiction, relationship problems, and low self-esteem.

Dynamic Deep Meditation is another development, This is an ancient technique that I have adapted and modified for modern day application which is very simple to do yet effectively removes stress and tension overloads. I am currently working on my next book `*The User's Guide for Vibrant Living*'. I offer seminars, workshops and talks, for interested groups and organisations and am due shortly to release a set of therapeutic relaxation tapes.

Tom Bolton upon request gives talks, seminars, and workshops, plus weekend and long weekend courses on the following:

Stress management
Building self-confidence
Relaxation techniques and self-hypnosis
Past-life regression, healing and self-healing
Visualisation, affirmation and chart work
Communicating with the Unconscious for change
Self-development

These courses can be structured to the requirements of interested groups and organisations. For details and bookings for the above please apply to:

Courses with Tom Bolton
c/o Jackqueline
at Butterfly Promotions
Tel: (01709) 702900 Fax: (01709) 548358
E-mail butterfly.pro@virgin.net

Or write enclosing a s.a.e. to:

40 Quarry Field Lane Wickersley,
Rotherham,
South Yorkshire
S66 OEJ

Tom also does private individual consultations in Wirral. For these inquiries only, write enclosing your telephone/fax number and a S.A.E. together with details of your inquiry to:

Tom Bolton c/o The Haven,
161a Manor Road,
Wallasey, Merseyside,
L44 OEN.

Subject Index

Useful Addresses

Centre Training School of Hypnotherapy and Psychotherapy
145 Chapel Lane,
Longton,
Preston, Lancs. PR4 5NA
Telephone: (01772) 617663

National School of Hypnosis and Psychotherapy
28 Finsbury Park Road,
London. N4 2JX
Telephone 0171 359 6991

World Federation of Healing
Charity No 286066
Head Office
33 The Park,
Kingswood,
Bristol BS15 4BL

The Theosophical Society (England)
50 Gloucester Place,
London W1H 4EA
Telephone: 01719 359261

International Federation of Aromatherapists
4 Eastmearn Road,
West Dulwich,
London SE21 8HA.

The National Federation of Spiritual Healers
Old Manor Farm Studio
Church Street
Sunbury-on-Thames,
Middx. TW16 6RG
Telephone: 01932 783164

The White Eagle Lodge
Brewell Lane
Rake, Nr Liss.
Hants GU33 7HY
Telephone: 01730 893300

Crown House Publishing

(A division of The Anglo-American Book Company Ltd.)
Crown Buildings,
Bancyfelin,
Carmarthen SA33 5ND
Wales.
Telephone: 01267 211880 / 211886
Fax: 01267 211882

We trust you enjoyed this title from our range of bestselling books for academic and general readership. Our authors are professionals of many years' experience, all highly respected in their own field. We choose our books with care for their content and character, and for the value of their contribution of both new and updated material to their particular field. Here is a list of our other publications.

Figuring Out People: *Design Engineering With Meta-Programs*
by Bob G. Bodenhamer & L. Michael Hall   Paperback   £12.99

Gold Counselling: *A Practical Psychology With NLP*
by Georges Philips   Paperback   £14.99

Grieve No More, Beloved: *The Book Of Delight*
by Ormond McGill   Hardback   £9.99

Influencing With Integrity: *Management Skills For Communication & Negotiation*
by Genie Z Laborde   Paperback   £12.50

Living Organisations: *Beyond The Learning Organisation*
by Lex McKee   Hardback   £16.99

The New Encyclopedia Of Stage Hypnotism
by Ormond McGill   Hardback   £29.99

The POWER Process: *An NLP Approach To Writing*
by Sid Jacobson & Dixie Elise Hickman   Paperback   £12.99

Scripts & Strategies In Hypnotherapy
by Roger P. Allen   Hardback   £19.99

The Secrets Of Magic: *Communicational Excellence For The 21st Century*
by L. Michael Hall   Paperback   £14.99

Seeing The Unseen: *A Past Life Revealed Through Hypnotic Regression*
by Ormond McGill   Paperback   £12.99

Slimming With Pete: *Taking The Weight Off Body AND Mind*
by Pete Cohen & Judith Verity   Paperback   £9.99

Solution States: *A Course In Solving Problems In Business Using NLP*
by Sid Jacobson   Paperback   £12.99

The Spirit Of NLP: *The Process, Meaning And Criteria For Mastering NLP*
by L. Michael Hall   Paperback   £12.99

Time-Lining: *Patterns For Adventuring In "Time"*
by Bob G. Bodenhamer & L. Michael Hall   Paperback   £14.99